Includes Scripture Confessions & Prayers for Your Baby
Plus, Developmental Highlights and Lots of Practical Advice

Birth Right®

God's Plan for
Your Pregnancy Journey

by
Julie Werner BS, HES

16 15 14 13 12 11   10 9 8 7 6 5 4 3 2 1

Birth Right
ISBN 10: 1-60683-348-0
ISBN 13: 978-1-60683-348-3
Copyright © 2011 by Julie Werner
Tulsa, Oklahoma 74145

Published by Harrison House Publishers
P.O. Box 35035
Tulsa, Oklahoma 74153
www.harrisonhouse.com

Table of Contents

Dedication

To my heavenly Father who blesses me not because I am good, but because He is. I give You all the praise and glory for every blessing in my life. On my own, I am nothing. I live and breathe because of You!

To my husband and boys – You are my greatest joy in life. I am honored to be your wife and mother.

To my parents – Thank you for raising me up in the way I should go so that when I am old, I will not depart from it. I can't thank you enough for your love, grace and most of all for showing me how to walk by the Word.

To my in-laws – Thank you for believing in me and for your constant prayers and support.

To Troy – thank you for allowing me this opportunity and believing in what God has placed in my heart.

To the HH team – Christian, Lisa, Christina, Gary, Tina and Christy B. – Thank you. It's an honor to work with you.

To Leah, my editor, thank you for all the countless facebook chats and emails. You helped me through this!

To Cindy, my wonderful proofreader who never lets me down!

And to Sara and Jenn who inspired this book – I love you both so much. Thank you for allowing your stories to minister to others.

Prologue

A friend of mine with six children defined a birth plan for me as a personalized document clarifying the mother's preferences for labor, birth and postpartum care.

So, does God have a plan for your pregnancy, labor, birth, and beyond? **Absolutely!** He created your body to carry a baby and to birth one.

My heart in putting this book together is that you will see and understand that perfect plan. I want to share these promises, testimonies, and the faithfulness of our God in each situation, so that you can birth the right way-God's way.

The faithful love of the
LORD never ends!
His mercies never cease.
Great is his faithfulness;
his mercies begin afresh
each morning.

Lamentations 3:22-23

Introduction

As I stared at the pregnancy test that December night, I was both thrilled and terrified at the same time. I would soon learn that there are many conflicting emotions along this journey of pregnancy. So many questions ran through my mind:

Who do I tell first? Do I tell anybody right now? What if it's wrong? I need to go get another test, or two or three... Thank You Jesus for this gift! Help me Jesus!

I went immediately to the Internet. Wow –was that a big shock! There were so many pregnancy websites and forums and message boards. How would I ever read all this information in one night? I didn't, of course, but I went back in the morning and at night and in the middle of the night, even.

How could there be so much information on a brief nine month period of someone's life? Well, I learned two things. Pregnancy is way more than a brief nine-month period: It is a life-changing journey and everyone has an opinion!

Fast forward eight years later and I have not only had two kids of my own, but I have watched my family members, friends, neighbors, and coworkers go through this life-changing journey. I have seen it sometimes take them to places that they never thought they would go.

How could something that God created to be so natural be so unnatural sometimes? I have watched family members go through miscarriages and fertility treatments. I have watched friends have their babies far too early and have to leave them in the hospital NICU for months. I have watched a coworker have a stillborn baby.

But, I have also seen the good. I have watched friends who were told they would never have babies have them. I have seen adoptive parents get pregnant after 17 years. I have watched God open the womb and bless a family with a child even when everything natural was done to prevent pregnancy.

Through it all, I have seen that God is faithful. His Word never changes and He is true to everything that He says. I compiled these stories so that you could know that you are not alone. Even if your situation is not covered in this book, God promises you in Hebrews 13:5 that He will never fail you or abandon you.

Remember, through this journey, He is always by your side.

Now – let's go!

Chapter 1

"My Story"

The year that I celebrated my 32nd birthday, life was good. My husband and I had an almost four year old and a ten month old. They were healthy and happy. I loved my job. I couldn't think of anything that I needed or wanted for my birthday. As I was praying and thanking the Lord for another year, my mind began to drift to two people very close to my heart.

The first was my sister. She had experienced many female problems in just her four years of marriage. She hadn't expressed her desire to get pregnant but I knew it had to be there. The other was a close friend of mine from college. She had been through a series of health problems since she was 17. She had been told by doctors that she would never carry a baby, yet she longed to be a mother.

I wanted to be able to give these ladies a baby so badly. I knew that if I wanted to be able to give them the gift of motherhood, then how much more did their heavenly Father want to give that gift to them?

At that point, I knew what I wanted for my birthday. I prayed that my sister and friend would be mothers by my next birthday and I didn't tell anybody. This was just between me and God. Imagine my surprise when my sister ended up pregnant less than two months later and then imagine my disappointment when she miscarried.

My friend had begun thinking of other avenues and was pursing possible adoption. She had been connected with a young, scared, pregnant teenager in high school who wanted to give up her baby. The teenager had met with my friend several times and felt that my friend was to be the mother of her unborn baby. She knew she could give the baby a good home and a future. This was now the summer of 2008 and my next birthday was coming close. In my narrow mind, I felt that at least one of them had a chance of becoming a mother before my birthday.

I was saddened to learn by text message, while on vacation, that the young lady my friend had been in contact with, had an abortion done that week. My friend was heartbroken, as was I for her.

My sister spent my birthday the next year getting her second D&C of the year after her second miscarriage. I remember thinking that this was the worst birthday ever.

But God!

Within a few weeks of my birthday, I got a text from my friend that said she took a pregnancy test and it was positive! (Well, actually it said "Holy Cow, it's positive".) She had some challenges in her pregnancy that God helped her overcome. You can read her story on pg 76.

My sister started having some good news as well. She began seeing a wonderful fertility doctor and within a few months, she was pregnant. God was working behind the scenes – just not on my time frame. I was so excited because my friend was due in April and my sister in July, just a week before my birthday. You can read my sister, Sara's story on pg 33. I knew that by this next birthday, my prayer would be answered.

You may be wondering if it is God's will for you to have a child. I have heard this question asked many times. The best way to answer this question is to go to the Scriptures. I like these scriptures specifically:

Take delight in the LORD, and he will give you your heart's desires. (Psalm 37:4)

Every good action and every perfect gift is from God. These good gifts come down from the Creator of the sun, moon, and stars, who does not change like their shifting shadows. James 1:17 NCV

The thief's purpose is to steal and kill and destroy. My purpose is to give them a rich and satisfying life. (John 10:10)

Don't you see that children are GOD's best gift? The fruit of the womb his generous legacy? Like a warrior's fistful of arrow are the children of a vigorous youth. Oh, how blessed are you parents, with your quivers full of children? Your enemies don't stand a chance against you; you'll sweep them right off your doorstep. (Psalm 127:3-5 MSG)

In the Scriptures, we see that God wants to give us our heart's desire, that every good gift is from Him, that He comes to give a rich and satisfying life, and that children are His best gift. Since God is no respecter of persons and does not show favoritism (Acts 10:34), we can draw the conclusion that the answer is a big YES! He wants to bless you and give you what your heart desires. He is not the author of stealing or killing or destroying. That is not the God we serve.

Let's take a look at two of the most well known women in the Bible who prayed for children.

Sarah is the first and she was married to Abraham. Genesis 16:1 says, "Now Sarai, Abram's wife, had borne him no children"(NIV). An interesting side note here is that God later changed Abram's name to Abraham which means "father of a multitude". He changed Sarai's name to Sarah, which means in that context "a mother of nations" (Genesis 17:15-16). God changed their names knowing that they would have a son, even though they couldn't fathom it yet.

Even though God had promised Abraham a son, as he and Sarah got older and it still hadn't happened, Sarah resorted to offering her Egyptian slave girl to her husband so that he could have a son through her. Even though she was trying to be sacrificial and give Abraham a son even if he wasn't hers, it wasn't God's best. God told Abraham that He would bless Sarah and make her a mother of nations. Abraham laughed because of their age. He was 100 years old and Sarah was 90 years old! Sarah was listening at the tent door and also laughed (Genesis. 18:12). But God responded by saying "Is anything too hard for the LORD?" (Genesis 18:13,14).

From that moment on, things were different and their faith was rewarded:

By faith even Sarah herself received ability to conceive, even beyond the proper time of life, since she considered Him faithful who had promised. (Hebrews 11:11 NASB)

They had a son named Isaac, which means "laughter". Sarah's laugh of doubt had turned into a laugh of joy and victory.

The other example in the Bible of a woman who prayed for a child is Hannah. She served God and loved Him, but she was childless. Her husband had two wives and the other wife had children. Each year, her husband, Elkanah, would go to offer a sacrifice to the Lord before the priests. He always gave Hannah a double portion of the sacrifice because he loved her and because she was barren. In I Samuel 1:7, we see that she went to the temple and cried out to the Lord and prayed. She was so emotional during her crying out to God that the priest actually thought she was drunk! She asked the Lord for a child and promised to give the child back to the Lord all the days of his life.

Hannah did become pregnant over the course of time and gave birth to a son that she named Samuel. She did give him over to the Lord at an early age and took him to the temple to be trained in the ways of God. When she brought Samuel to the temple, she said to the priest," I am the woman that stood by thee here, praying unto the LORD. For this child I prayed; and the LORD hath given me my petition which I asked of him" (1 Samuel 1:26-27 KJV).

With both Sarah and Hannah, I think it's important to note that most of the time, getting pregnant doesn't happen on our time schedule. Sometimes, it seems that we can make the act of getting pregnant a "work". Jesus came to give us rest. In Matthew 11:28, He says, "Come to me, all of you who are weary and carry heavy burdens, and I will give you rest." Knowing and tracking the right times of the month to be with your husband is fine, but when it becomes a burden or a stress, I don't believe that is the will of God. Trust in Him. Do what you know to do and leave the rest up to Him. He won't disappoint you.

Jesus said, "If you ask for anything in my name, I will do it for you so that the Father's glory will be shown through the Son" (John 14:13 NCV). He wants to give you the desires of your heart. He is your Daddy. He loves you. Just ask Him.

I Want a Baby

by Marnie

I was diagnosed with PCOS (Polycystic Ovarian Syndrome) in my early twenties – years before I even thought of having children. When my husband, Bryan, and I got married, we really did not discuss having children. I guess we were fine either way. In 2003, I was diagnosed with Lyme disease. It made me slow down from my hectic life as a veterinarian working 70 hour weeks. It was during that time that I felt a tug on my heart to be a momma. When I was 28, we started visiting an endocrinologist/reproductive specialist to see if he thought it was alright to get pregnant because of my lingering problems with Lyme disease.

The endocrinologist thought everything would be fine, but counseled us again about how infertility would affect our quest to become parents. We tried for about six months without any success. I was then placed on oral fertility meds. We were pregnant within three months. The month that I got pregnant, my doctor told me that it was not a great ovulation and that it would likely not be a positive outcome. When we asked him about the chance of multiples, he said that we had less than a one percent chance of having twins.

When we went for the ultrasound at six weeks, I could not believe my eyes when I saw TWO gestational sacs. In our moment of joy, my doctor made the statement-- "this is starting out as a twin pregnancy". He was not confident that twin B would survive because the gestational sac was so much smaller than that of twin A. At this point, we did not consider this a successful pregnancy unless we had healthy twins in the end.

My pregnancy progressed uneventfully and twin B caught up in size to twin A. I was fortunate to escape gestational diabetes and preeclampsia, which was almost unheard of in a twin pregnancy.

At 31 weeks, my water broke in the middle of the night. They made every attempt to stop my labor, but our twins were born on Father's Day 2005, nine weeks early. Blake (twin A) weighed 4 lbs 3 oz and Emmerson (twin B) weighed 3 lbs 7 oz. I was not prepared to see such tiny babies. The doctors told us that they would be in the NICU for at least nine weeks. I cannot explain the sadness we felt leaving our babies behind after I was discharged from the hospital. Once again, our twins proved to be super babies by leaving the NICU in just 10 days (twin A) and 14 days (twin B).

After a few years, my husband, Bryan, and I really felt the urge to expand our family. We worried about the possibility of twins and another premature delivery, but our doctors assured us that it was unlikely. We used oral fertility treatment again, but this time we became pregnant on the first try. My pregnancy with Griffin was very uneventful. He was born two and a half weeks early and weighed in at 8 lb 9 oz. When Griffin was a year old, we became pregnant again without the help of meds or doctors. Unfortunately, I miscarried at only five weeks along. I was so hurt and put a lot of blame on myself. But, God helped me get through that and told me I would share my testimony with others.

Within weeks, I was sharing my testimony at church and in our small women's group.

Little did I know that I would be pregnant again just a month after my miscarriage. Again, we were able to conceive without the help of doctors or meds. God is so faithful! When we went to the doctor at six weeks for our first ultrasound, he put the probe on my belly and a look of sadness came across his face when he was unable to detect a heartbeat. He told me that I would likely miscarry this baby as well, and told me to go home and wait. So I went home, defeated and asking God why I had to go through this again! I decided a few days after that first ultrasound that I would fight and pray for this baby. I was this baby's momma and if I didn't fight for it then who would?

We went back for a recheck ultrasound one week after the initial ultrasound. When the doctor put the probe on my belly, I could see the little heart beating. I could not contain my tears of joy! Grey was born at 40 weeks weighing 8 lb 12 oz.

God took my infertility and turned it into a testimony. I cannot praise God enough for my four children who are "fearfully and wonderfully made".

I praise you because I am fearfully and wonderfully made;
your works are wonderful and I know that full well.
Psalm 139: 14 NIV

I'll Do Anything to Be a Mommy

by Paula

Nine years of marriage without kids, plus two fertility doctors, plus one laparoscopy, plus six months of induced menopause, plus one cycle of fertility drugs with self-administered shots, plus one trigger shot, plus one C-section, equals baby boy #1. One year later: two cycles of fertility drugs with self-administered shots, plus six months of induced menopause, plus three cycles of fertility drugs with self-administered shots, plus one trigger shot, plus artificial insemination, plus one C-section, equals baby boy #2. This is what it took for us to have children.

When we were first married, we had no idea that it would be nine years before we had our first child. But through the waiting and disappointments, prayers of family and friends sustained us and were answered in God's timing, not ours. God's blessings are numerous and our hearts are full of thankfulness not only for our two boys, but for how our trials helped us discover who God really is. We did learn a few things while on our journey.

GOD KNOWS WHAT IS BEST FOR HIS CHILDREN

It took us four years to conceive our first child and two and a half to conceive our second. During that time, we had questions of why and what if --- Why could most women get pregnant so easily and even plan their pregnancies? Why did I have endometriosis and polycystic ovarian syndrome? Why had no other doctors diagnosed correctly? What if we could never have children? But after all the questions, we just had to trust that God would provide all that we needed and that we needed to trust in His always sufficient providence.

The questions turned into quiet trust as we continued treatment, knowing that if we never got pregnant, God was still good and had other plans for us, such as adoption. In the midst of our suffering, God used our experiences to strengthen us spiritually and to daily draw us closer to Him.

GOD ANSWERS PRAYERS IN UNEXPECTED WAYS

After many consultations and fertility drugs, my first doctor was unable to help us conceive. In the midst of that frustration, I cried out to God, wondering what the next step was supposed to be. I was already an emotional wreck and we had just begun! Were we supposed to start looking for another doctor right away, or should we take a break? We decided the best thing for us at this time would be to stop seeing that doctor and just wait. Not long after we decided this, two of my friends (at the same time!) who were also unable to get pregnant had both found a doctor they liked whom they recommended to us. This was an answer to prayer I hadn't expected so soon! This doctor ended up being the doctor who was able to help me conceive and who also delivered both of our babies.

NO MATTER WHAT IS HAPPENING, THANKFULNESS
SHOULD BE DAILY IN OUR PRAYERS

Hannah offered a song of thanksgiving in I Samuel 2 as did Mary in Luke 1. Always be thankful to the One who created life! "There is no one holy like the LORD; there is no one besides you; there is no Rock like our God" (I Samuel 2:2 NIV).

HOW MY SPIRIT REJOICES IN GOD MY SAVIOR! FOR HE TOOK NOTICE OF HIS LOWLY SERVANT GIRL, AND FROM NOW ON ALL GENERATIONS WILL CALL ME BLESSED. FOR THE MIGHTY ONE IS HOLY, AND HE HAS DONE GREAT THINGS FOR ME.
Luke 1:47-49

A Journey with a Detour

by Brandi

Growing up, all I ever wanted to be was a mother. I was everyone's babysitter, worked in the church nursery, and played with all the baby cousins. It was truly my heart's desire to get married and become a mother. The devil tried everything in his power to take this dream away but my God had other plans.

My husband, JD, and I met when I was 15 and he was 18, but we didn't start dating for another three years. I knew I wanted to marry this man early on in the relationship. He was and is my best friend. JD proposed to me on Christmas Day 2002, and we were married the following September.

In January 2004, I went in for my annual gynecology appointment and found out that I had Polycystic Ovarian Syndrome (PCOS). I was told at the age of 21 that the chances of us conceiving naturally were slim to none and we would more than likely have to use fertility drugs. I was devastated at first, but after talking and praying with JD, we decided that we would give it over to God and follow His path for our family. We also decided that we were still young and weren't quite ready to go the fertility drug path. That May, we started actively trying to conceive a baby. It was hard each month waiting to see if we were pregnant. We went through A LOT of pregnancy tests.

We continued to pray daily for a family. Growing up in church, I was always taught the power in our words so I hung notes on my bathroom mirror that had scriptures like

Mark 11:24 and declarations that said "I AM PREGNANT!" I spoke these confessions and scriptures over my body daily. Also when people would say things along the lines of "I'm sorry you can't get pregnant," I would respond with, "Oh it is not that I can't, it is just that I haven't yet" or "Oh, I will get pregnant in God's timing." I never gave up on my dream of being a mother, no matter what people said.

In January, it came time for my annual appointment again. We decided to get a second opinion from a new doctor. This year we were told we would HAVE to use fertility drugs to conceive. We still weren't ready for that step so we just gave it all to God again.

Over the next few years, we struggled with our infertility every month. Every month our hopes would rise with the possibility of a pregnancy and all would come crashing down with each negative test. We never gave up even when all the doctors told us we couldn't do it.

In October 2008, JD and I got guardianship of my two youngest siblings. We started focusing on the kids and giving them a stable home. In March 2009, I began becoming dizzy and extremely tired all the time. My breasts were also very tender. After a few weeks of these symptoms, I decided that I would take a test. I bought a double pack thinking I could take one now, and if it came up negative then I would have one to take first thing the next morning. I was out running errands for the day and had to run into the mall for something, so I grabbed one of the tests since I needed to go to the restroom.

Once in there, I decided just to get it over with, knowing it would probably say "Not Pregnant" again. So there in the public restroom at the local mall, I got my first ever positive pregnancy test. I was shocked, excited, and nervous, all at once. I wandered around in circles at the mall for a little while trying to figure out just how to tell my husband that we were finally pregnant.

I bought a card for JD that had something to do with a baby, signed it "Love, your wife and Baby C," and went to find him at work. He didn't get it at first, but then I showed him the test and he was speechless. Later on that evening, while waiting on JD's parents to come over to tell them our news, JD asked me to take the other test. At first I was confused, but then he explained that he had never seen a test come up positive and really wanted to see that. So I took the other test and when it came up positive, he grabbed me and gave me the biggest hug. From that point forward, we told anyone and everyone that would listen that we were pregnant.

We had our first doctor's appointment and ultrasound on April 3rd. It was so amazing to see our little jelly bean up on that screen. Seeing that heart blinking so fast just left me speechless and in tears of joy. We found out that we were due around November 23rd. I had a very easy pregnancy for the most part-- no morning sickness but a lot of heartburn. Around the end of June, I started swelling, but nothing too bad. July 22nd was a big day as we finally found out that the baby was a boy! We were so excited and decided on the name Nolan James. During this visit, we found out that his measurements were a little off but the doctor wasn't too worried about it at that point and said they would just measure again at the next appointment.

On August 18th, at 26 weeks gestation, I went in for my routine monthly appointment. They did another ultrasound and discovered Nolan's measurements were even more off than at the last appointment. From there they sent me to the lab to run a ton of tests, and they drew 18 vials of blood; I didn't think they were ever going to stop. I was also referred to a specialist to see if we could figure out exactly what was going on with Nolan.

The following week, we met with Dr. B, the specialist. There, they ran a more indepth ultrasound, from which we learned that Nolan's placenta didn't form correctly. Instead of the placenta growing flat against my uterus with the umbilical cord in the middle, the placenta grew up around the umbilical cord, causing Nolan to not get all the nutrients he needed to grow properly. It was decided that from then until the end of the pregnancy, I would be seeing Dr. B and my regular doctor every week to be able to monitor Nolan's growth more closely.

At my next appointment, my blood pressure was a little on the high side, but I didn't have any protein in my urine so they told me just to watch it and as long as it didn't go over 140/90 then that was fine. I also found out the results of some of the blood work. It had come back that my body wasn't absorbing folic acid the way it is supposed to and that I had a blood clotting disease called thrombophilia type II. As a result, I was prescribed a new prenatal vitamin with more folic acid and baby aspirin to help with the blood clotting.

Two days later, while picking up my prescriptions at the pharmacy, I took my blood pressure and it was 143/89. Since the doctor's office was closed for the evening, I decided to wait till the next morning to call them. September 3rd, I called the doctor's office to report my blood pressure from the previous night, and was told to go have it checked again.

I was nervous all the way to the pharmacy, but continued to pray that it would be in a normal range. Unfortunately, it was higher than the night before, so off to the doctor's office I went. Once again, they took my blood pressure; it had risen even higher than it had been at the pharmacy that morning. My doctor then decided that it would be best for me to be admitted into the hospital so that I could be closely monitored. I was devastated to say the least, but after calling my husband and family to let them know what was going on, I refocused on my goal of keeping Nolan in as long as possible.

At 28 weeks and 3 days gestation, I was admitted into the hospital with my husband by my side. We were both nervous but confident in our doctors and the plan God had for our family. The first test they ran was a 24-hour urine collection for preeclampsia. It came back showing I had a slight case (around 1200) and that meant that I would be in the hospital for the remainder of my pregnancy. I asked my doctor if the preeclampsia numbers ever went down and was told that anything was possible but not to count on that happening. My doctors ordered daily ultrasounds to keep an eye on the blood flow in Nolan's umbilical cord, my daily input/output, biweekly blood draws, vitals taken every three hours, twice a day monitoring of Nolan's heart rate & movement, steroids to help develop Nolan's lungs, an IV for fluids, and eventually a PICC line.

A few days after the first 24-hour test, the doctors ordered another one. My family and I began to pray and believe that those numbers would come way down. When the results came in and showed that my number had come down by almost half, my doctors were shocked to say the least. Although it wasn't enough to allow me to go home, it was great to see an answer to our prayers. I saw at least two doctors a day, along with countless nurses and nurses' aides. Family and friends came by to keep me company and my spirits up.

After a couple of weeks, Nolan started to show signs of stress with lower amounts of blood flowing through his umbilical cord and his heart rate started to drop every now and then during the monitoring. We went ahead and planned a C-section for September 29th and went on a tour of the NICU. At 31 weeks and 3 days, Nolan's heart rate dropped one too many times and I was taken to Labor and Delivery to be monitored for 12 hours.

It was decided the next morning to go ahead with the C-section that day. With my husband by my side, I was prepped for surgery. Shortly after it began, my doctor said "Now that explains a lot…" but said nothing else until after I was back in recovery. My husband, who was sitting by my head, exclaimed, "I see him! I see him!" Nolan was born at 31 weeks, 4 days on September 25th at 1:14pm weighing in at 2lbs 10oz and was 14 1/2 inches long. He was breathing on his own but was struggling just a little so he was placed on the ventilator to help him. He was just a little bigger than JD's hand, but still so tiny. They bundled him up and brought him over for me to see. It was love at first sight.

JD went with Nolan down to the NICU while they sewed me back up and sent me back to Labor and Delivery to recover. While I was in recovery, my doctor came in to explain what they had found during the surgery. Evidently, only the left side of my uterus developed. I have two ovaries and two fallopian tubes, but only the left ones are attached to the uterus. So I only have one working ovary and it has PCOS. Nolan was a miracle in every way possible-malformed placenta, my high blood pressure, and just half the room to grow in. JD took some pictures of Nolan for me to see since I couldn't get out of bed till the next day. He was doing really well and I couldn't wait to go see him and touch him.

Nolan was off the ventilator before 9:00 A.M. the next morning. When I got to see him for the first time, I couldn't believe just how tiny he was. His diapers were no bigger than a Kotex. He had an IV, a feeding tube, nasal oxygen tube, pulse oximeter, was on caffeine to help him to keep his heart rate up, and had leads measuring his breathing and heart rate. Nolan was doing well but had a long road ahead of him. I didn't get to hold him until he was 4 days old and it was the most amazing experience of my life. We did what is called "kangaroo care," which is where they placed him inside my shirt with nothing but a diaper on. This helped Nolan regulate his body temperature along with his breathing and heart rate by matching mine.

After an almost three-week stay in the hospital, I was released and had to go home without my baby. Once again, the devil tried to steal my joy of being a mother, but I continued to focus on God, knowing that my baby would come home soon. Nolan lost down to 2lbs 5oz a few days after birth, but other than the initial weight loss, he only lost weight a few other times. He had several head ultrasounds looking for brain bleeds that are common in preemies and passed all them with flying colors.

Nolan started out taking 3ml of breastmilk via feeding tube every three hours and was slowly increased over the next couple of months. Every day, I would be at the hospital by his 11 A.M. feeding, would stay through the 2 P.M. feeding, get home in time for my older kids (my siblings) to come home from school and then after dinner would head back up to the hospital for the 8 P.M. feeding. At one month of age, Nolan was weighing in at 3lbs 12.7oz, he was taking more and more of his feeds by bottle, and had upgraded to regular preemie size diapers. He was still on his oxygen, caffeine, and had to have a blood transfusion, but overall was doing extremely well.

Over the next few weeks, Nolan got closer and closer to coming home. In order to do this, he had to pass a car seat tolerance test, a sleep study, take all his feeds by bottle, and weigh around 5 lbs. JD and I had to take a CPR class also. As we grew closer to coming home, we decided not to tell anyone until he was home so that we could have a quiet homecoming. On November 12, he passed his car seat test and the next step was the sleep test.

On November 15th, Nolan weighed in at 4lbs 15.2oz and started his sleep study that night. The next day, we were anxious to get to the hospital to see if he passed. As we walked in to the NICU, all the nurses were just as excited as we were. The results came back borderline abnormal which just meant that he would go home on his caffeine and a heart monitor.

That day was a long day as we had to wait to have his pictures taken, prescriptions filled, get the heart monitor, and learn how to use it. When we finally went to leave the NICU, it was bittersweet. On one hand, we were totally ready to be done with the hospital but on the other hand after seven weeks in the NICU, we had become very attached to our wonderful doctors and nurses.

As we pulled out of the parking garage, JD looked at me and said, "Why don't you call your mom & dad and see if they want to come hold their new grandson?" and so I did.

Nolan is now a healthy toddler and gets into everything! Other than a double hernia surgery at three months old, he is a very healthy baby. We are currently in the process of adopting my two youngest siblings and look for it to be finalized this year. Growing up, when I pictured my family, this isn't what I had in mind but God did and His picture is so much better. I thank God daily for giving me my family.

> He is like a rock; what he does is perfect,
> and he is always fair. He is a faithful God
> who does no wrong, who is right and fair.
> Deuteronomy 32:4 NCV

Chapter 2

Miscarriages, Prematurity and a Bad Diagnosis

I have had lots of my friends go through tough times trying to be a mom and even as moms. I shared with you the stories of my friend and sister. Even though all of that was tough to walk through, when they finally did become mothers, it was that much sweeter.

I also have close friends who have gone through premature births. If you have ever walked through that, then you know that it isn't easy. Leaving your baby in the NICU while you go home has to be one of the hardest things to ever go through. It's unnatural.

Lastly, I have some friends who received a bad diagnosis when they were pregnant. They went for a normal appointment or ultrasound, only to find out that something was very wrong with their baby.

One message that I want to get across very clearly is that God is not in the baby-stealing business. God is blamed for so much and I detest the statements:

- **God needed another angel**
- **It was his/her time**
- **God has a plan**

Of course God has a plan and that is that every person lives out their days on the earth. Why would God give you a baby in your womb only to take it right back? That makes no sense.

I certainly do not have all the answers for premature birth, miscarriage, or for physical disabilities, but I can guarantee you, God is not the cause! John 10:10 gives us the job descriptions of both the devil and Jesus: The thief which is the devil does not come except to steal, and to kill, and to destroy. I [Jesus Christ] have come that they may have life, and that they may have it more abundantly.

If you stop and think about it, a baby is a gift straight from the heavenly Father. The enemy wants to do everything in his power to make sure babies are miscarried, deformed, and sick. He wants to try everything possible to make sure there isn't one more person on this earth serving God and winning people to the Lord.

There is good news, however! We win! We have the victory over death and Satan. We serve the living God! Know today that God wants you to have your heart's desires and He wants to give you precious gifts.

He is for you and not against you (Romans 8:31). Read these testimonies and be encouraged as you see His heart for you.

Where's My Happy Ending?

by Sara

Two weeks after marrying the man of my dreams, I began having some female problems. I immediately saw my OB/GYN and she wanted to do surgery to remove a softball size cyst on my right ovary. My husband and I both felt uneasy about the surgery because she was almost certain that the right ovary would have to be removed also, so instead we opted for another procedure that never completely removed the cyst, but only kept it at a minimal size. I underwent three of these procedures over the next three years and had been told by doctors that the right ovary would never be able to function properly.

We had come to the conclusion in our own minds that having children might not be in our future and we were both fine with that UNTIL September 2007 when I found out I was pregnant. That is all I have to say about that because every woman knows that the minute you see the positive sign, everything changes. Your hopes and your dreams all include that sweet baby that is growing inside of you. You long to hold something that you have never laid eyes on and in your heart, you ARE a momma. Unfortunately, this pregnancy ended in a fetal demise at nine weeks. We were heartbroken but found comfort and hope in God's Word and found out that it WAS His will for us to have a healthy child.

After that pregnancy, we WANTED children. We tried for 7 months and then started fertility treatments with a faith-filled doctor. We began treatments and became pregnant again and it also led to a fetal demise around nine weeks. That summer I read Joseph Prince's book, *Destined to Reign*, and found out what grace was really all about. This whole time, our hope was not in anything but the word because all else had failed, even the specialists. We refused to give up, reading and quoting scriptures like "Delight yourself in the LORD and he will give you the desires of your heart (Psalm 37:4 NIV) day and night over my body and our unborn child. We also rested in the fact that Jesus had already paid the way for my body to be whole and we trusted fully in Him. We realized that He wanted to bless us, not because of anything we had done, but because He is good and loves us.

Two months later, our doctor decided to do a very expensive type of treatment that required extremely precise timing. We had planned on having artificial insemination on day 15 of my menstrual cycle. On the first day, I found a lump under my armpit and by day 11, it was the size of a golf ball. We knew that this was just a distraction from the enemy, but we had to do what the doctor said. He was uncertain of this mass's etiology and without a biopsy to make that determination didn't want to proceed. We felt like there was no way to do everything within four days. I went to see a surgeon on day 11 and he said, "We will take it out tomorrow and do a biopsy." We were so excited.

The mass was removed and was proven to be benign and I was on my way to have IUI (Intrauterine Insemination). We got there that day to have the procedure done and the doctor performed the ultrasound and declared, "I'm not going to waste your money. Go home and you will be pregnant by Saturday." He was right. About 10 days later, I found out that I was pregnant with our beautiful daughter who was born on July 11, 2009. God is faithful! He loves us so much and is always looking to bless us with His gifts. Just receive them!

Every good and perfect gift is from above, coming down from the Father of the heavenly lights, who does not change like shifting shadows. James 1:17 NIV

But It's Too Early...

by Mariana

"God is not going to give me more than I can handle," is what I told myself repeatedly during the days that led up to my daughter's birth and the weeks that followed. At 27½ weeks pregnant, I was hospitalized with preeclampsia. Specialists came to prepare me for the inevitable; I was going to deliver early, and they wanted me to be as prepared as possible. At that point, the goal was to keep from delivering until I was 30 to 32 weeks pregnant. This broke my heart, because even then the baby was not ready to be born. It just wasn't time yet! I pleaded with God. If only He would let me go full term. If only He would perform a miracle. And that is exactly what He did, just not in the way I expected.

I made it to 28 weeks into the pregnancy. That Wednesday night, I called my husband to come back to the hospital after taking our son home because I was in so much pain and knew something was very wrong. My body had gone into HELLP syndrome, but we didn't know it yet. When the blood work finally came back to show that my liver was shutting down, it was decided that the baby would need to be delivered immediately. I remember lying in the bed in so much pain, feeling so guilty, because at that point, I just wanted it to be over. I hated that my body was rejecting my baby, and kept asking God why He would design my body to have a baby but then not allow me to take care of it until the baby was fully developed. I tried to find some reason for this happening. What could I have done differently throughout the pregnancy? No answer came.

My miracle—Adalyn Grace—was born Thursday at 3:50 A.M. at 28 weeks and one day gestation. She weighed 1 lb 14 oz. and was 13 ¾ inches long. She came out crying! When the nurses wheeled her by me in the operating room, she was flailing, but I didn't know what that was at the time. All I saw was my tiny, little, baby girl waving at me, and I knew that she and I would be fine. Adalyn was never on a ventilator, and that in itself was a miracle, considering how small she was. She had very few setbacks during her nine week stay in the NICU. This little girl was so covered in prayer and she grew and developed. I watched my baby develop outside of the womb instead of feeling her grow like most mothers.

As I watched Adalyn grow and waited for her to come home, I spent much time in prayer. I felt a lot of guilt over what had happened, even though I knew that I couldn't have done anything about it. It was days before I could go into her room and see her without crying. But God worked on my heart. One day I heard someone ask why we always ask, "God, why me?" She then followed by, "Why not me? Why would I ever wish this on someone else?" This changed me.

God had promised me in Philippians 4:13 that I can do all things through Christ. And I knew that all of this would work together for my good (Romans 8:28). I knew that God had a special plan for my little girl, and he was confident that we could handle this through Him. Therefore, I spoke healing scriptures and prayed over Adalyn. I read her stories. I talked to her. I sang to her. I tried to make our situation as "normal" as possible.

About a week had gone by when I stood over her one day and for the first time, felt indescribable love for her. Life had changed. It wasn't what her daddy and I had planned. We were not ready for her, like she was not ready to be born, but it was okay. We had God on our side, family and friends that supported us, and a beautiful daughter who was healthy and growing. To God be the glory!

> And we know that God causes everything to work together for the good of those who love God and are called according to his purpose for them.
> Romans 8:28

Bad News
by Katie

In January 2003, I was almost five months pregnant with our first child. My husband and I were so excited to find out what we were having and couldn't wait for our ultrasound appointment. The day came and we were thrilled to learn that we were having a boy! We had already picked out the name Max. Once my husband found out it was a boy, there was no more discussion; his name was Max. We called everyone we could think of to tell them the good news. We had no idea of the news we would receive in just a few short days.

At my follow up appointment with my OB/GYN, he went over the results of the ultrasound, including the length, approximate weight, sex of the baby, etc. I noticed the words "choroid cyst" written and circled in red on the chart the doctor was holding. I asked what that meant. My doctor was brief in his explanation, as to not scare me, and said that he wanted to schedule another ultrasound in eight weeks to check on the cysts.

I went back to work overwhelmed with disbelief. How could there be something wrong with this precious baby God had given me? Once in the privacy of my office, I logged on to the Internet to find out what choroid cysts were. After only ten or fifteen minutes of research, I had more information than I ever cared to know about the subject. It turned out that these cysts could be markers for Edwards syndrome, which is a chromosomal disorder similar to Down's Syndrome. I couldn't read anymore. I was shaking. I turned off the computer and started to pray.

When I got home that night, I told my husband John what the doctor had said and what I had found out on the Internet. We decided to pray. We both felt led to not tell anybody because we did not want to speak that diagnosis over our son. It was hard. I didn't even tell my mom, and I tell her everything. It was the longest eight weeks of my life, and no one knew what we were going through.

At 28 weeks of pregnancy, I went back to the doctor for a follow up ultrasound, and the cysts were completely gone! We were so happy and gave God all the glory! Max was born on June 18, 2003, and was perfectly healthy, even after being born not breathing. Today, Max is an intelligent, energetic, eight year old, who loves Jesus and hunting and fishing.

Fast forward over seven years later, and I was shocked to learn we were expecting our third baby, after thinking we were done. We had one boy and one girl, but the Lord had other plans. When we went for the 20-week ultrasound, we were also told that our son, Alexander, had choroid plexus cysts on both sides of his brain. The specialist was very discouraging and even showed me a website that explained how these cysts can sometimes be a sign of Trisomy 18. Trisomy 18 is also called Edwards syndrome and occurs in about 1:3000 live births. Unlike Down's syndrome, Trisomy 18 is usually fatal, with most of the babies dying before birth and those who do make it to birth typically living only a few days. He made this disorder sound inevitable.

At first, this report didn't move me at all. I thought to myself, *"Okay, God healed Max. He can heal Alexander, too."* But, in the amount of time it took to get from the doctor's office to my house, I was a mess. I was crying. I started doubting whether God really did heal Max, or if it was just by chance that the cysts went away. I started dwelling on the images of the babies the doctor had shown me on the website. I thought that the cysts must be more serious this time because they didn't send me to a specialist last time, and the doctor didn't give me any information about the disorder with Max.

When I got home, my husband and I once again agreed not to say anything to anyone, and we would believe God to heal again. I got in the Word, and God gave me a verse on which to stand. It was Proverbs 21:30 KJV which reads, "There is no wisdom nor understanding nor counsel against the LORD." I knew God's report was that my pregnancy would go well, and my baby would be healthy. No matter what the "specialist" said, there is no counsel against the Lord. We had to go back to the specialist at 28 weeks just like with Max and of course, all the cysts were gone. Praise God! He is faithful! Alexander was born on August 24, 2010, perfectly healthy and whole.

If you receive a bad report, know it is not the last report. God has the final word.

It is the same with my word. I send it out, and it always produces fruit. It will accomplish all I want it to, and it will prosper everywhere I send it.
Isaiah 55:11

Chapter 3

In Vitro Fertilization (IVF)

According to Wikipedia.org, in vitro fertilization is defined as the process by which egg cells are fertilized by sperm outside the body. IVF is a major infertility treatment that is utilized when other methods of assisted reproductive technology have failed.

Basically, IVF creates a "test tube baby". Fertility specialists take eggs from the woman's ovaries during ovulation and take sperm from the man and fertilize them in a tube. Once they are fertilized and become an embryo or embryos, they are implanted into the uterus. IVF is not only complex, but it can also be very expensive as well.

I wanted to include a section on in vitro fertilization in this book because IVF is common to us now. We are living in a time where technology has grown by leaps and bounds. Can you imagine Sarah and Hannah in the Bible having the option of in vitro fertilization? It sounds funny, but so many women have to make that choice today.

Some women give their life's savings and take out their retirement early so that they can realize their dream of becoming a mother. Even after spending all the time and money on the procedure, the outcome of a baby isn't always guaranteed.

During my time of writing this book, I asked many women their thoughts on IVF. Although it can seem like such an unnatural procedure, God did give us the ability to think and create and to help others. The consensus with most of the women that I talked to is that if the Lord leads you to do IVF, then that is between you and Him and we aren't to say whether it is right or wrong.

However, I will point out something very interesting. While in the middle of this book project and in my conversations with many people about the subject, I found that most people never had to go as far as IVF. God always came through before they had to consider that option. I was even told the story of one lady's cousin who had IVF and then years later got pregnant on her own. I know of a distant relative that this happened to as well. I am sure that it could be a common story for many out there.

If you are facing the choice of having to do IVF, remember to do what you know in your heart is best for you and your family. When you pray and talk to the Lord about it, He will lead you in the right way. He knows all and sees all and only He can lead you in the right direction for a decision as big as this one. Make sure you are seeing a doctor who is in agreement with your choices and in whom you have confidence.

What is right for you may not be right for your best friend or your sister or cousin. Romans 14:23 NCV says, "But those who eat something without being sure it is right are wrong because they did not believe it was right. Anything that is done without believing it is right is a sin." That is why it is so important to seek God and hear the Holy Spirit leading you into His truth. Be sure and read the teaching on the Holy Spirit's leading in the Fear vs. Peace chapter of this book for more encouragement.

On that same note, I would like to point out that even when we mess up and blow it, God's grace is still there and we can fall into it without shame. Romans 8:1 tells us that there is now no condemnation for those who are in Christ Jesus. I also want to reach out to the women who have had an abortion in their past and are feeling like infertility is their punishment. This is a lie from the enemy.

Our heavenly Father loves you and wants only good things for you. He is not mad at you. He is standing with arms wide open to redeem your past. Psalm 36:5 tells us that His mercy reaches to the heavens. Nothing is too big for His grace.

Jeremiah 29:11-13 says, "'For I know the plans I have for you,' says the LORD. 'They are plans for good and not for disaster, to give you a future and a hope. In those days when you pray, I will listen. If you look for me wholeheartedly, you will find me.'"

God promises that if you look for Him with your whole heart, you will find Him. His plans for you are greater than your own, so don't fret or second guess yourself. He will lead you into the right decision for you. Trust Him and He won't let you down!

Chapter 4

Fear vs. Peace During Pregnancy

When I was in high school, my youth pastor defined fear as:

>   False
>   Evidence
>   Appearing
>   Real

This definition has stuck with me ever since. I think fear is probably the biggest hurdle that a woman faces during pregnancy. According to Webster's Dictionary, fear is defined as "a painful emotion or passion excited by the expectation of evil, or the apprehension of impending danger; apprehension; anxiety, solicitude; alarm ; dread." So the opposite of that would be peace, which is defined as "a state of quiet or tranquility, freedom from disturbance or agitation; calm; repose."

Our thoughts are so important to the outcome of situations in our lives. In 2 Corinthians 10:5, Paul tells us to capture rebellious thoughts and teach them to obey Christ. The first step in fighting fear is to stop those thoughts. It might be hard at first but the more you begin to fix your mind on the positive ("Set your minds on things above, not on earthly things" Colossians 3:2 NIV), the more you will drown out the negative thoughts.

As a mother, you want to be able to take care of your child and control what goes on around him or her. When your child is growing in the womb, you know that you cannot control everything. You can eat right and get plenty of rest, but in the end, you have to be able to give that worry to the Lord.

Psalm 55:22 says, "Give your burdens to the LORD, and he will take care of you. He will not permit the godly to slip and fall." First Peter 5:7 NIV reads, "Cast all your anxiety on him because he cares for you." These scriptures reflect God's heart for you. He wants you to give your worries and fears to Him so that you can enjoy your pregnancy.

In exchange for your worry and fear, you can have peace. The kind of peace that God gives is unexplainable. It's the kind of thing where you just know that everything is going to be ok, even if things look bleak. Philippians 4:6-7 says it best:

Don't worry about anything; instead, pray about everything. Tell God what you need, and thank him for all he has done. Then you will experience God's peace, which exceeds anything we can understand. His peace will guard your hearts and minds as you live in Christ Jesus.

Philippians 4:8 tells us to think on whatever is true, and honorable, and right, and pure, and lovely, and admirable and to think about things that are excellent and worthy of praise. When a negative thought that produces fear comes, begin to think about the things that are true and pure and lovely. Fill your mind with the Word and with thoughts of God's love and His desire to give you an abundant life.

While writing this book, I had a few of my close friends who had recently had babies over to my house. We talked about what expectant mothers might want to read and what was their biggest hurdle, fear, etc. To my surprise, I learned that there are some women out there who don't go to the Internet for every single symptom. Sometimes, you can be on the opposite side of fear and instead of worrying about things, you are confident in thinking, *That would never happen to me.*

This is mostly a good way to be. However, sometimes the confidence becomes over-confidence and you can possibly ignore signs from your body or even from baby.

I would encourage you that if you ever feel that something isn't right deep inside, to get it checked out. You don't have to feel bad about calling your doctor if you have questions. That is what they are there for. That's their job. Instead of being naïve, try to be proactive, all the while having peace. God has given you the Holy Spirit to quicken you and bring things to light. If you feel that the Holy Spirit is nudging you about something that isn't right, then take action.

Lots of times, people talk about a "gut feeling". That feeling is usually the Holy Spirit trying to warn us or speak to us about which way to go or what to do in a certain situation. Jesus said in John 15:26 NCV, "I will send you the Helper from the Father; he is the Spirit of truth who comes from the Father."

The Holy Spirit is our Helper and is the Spirit of truth. He will lead us into truth and peace as well. He does not reveal things to us to cause us fear, but to lead us in the right way. Jesus promises us that, "I have told you these things so that in me you may have peace. In this world you will have trouble. But take heart! I have overcome the world" (John 16:33 NIV).

I believe that John 14:25-26 NCV sums it up best:

> I have told you all these things while I am with you. But the Helper will teach you everything and will cause you to remember all that I told you. The Helper is the Holy Spirit whom the Father will send in my name.

The Holy Spirit dwells within us to teach us and to cause us to remember what Jesus said. Jesus wants us to take heart and to have peace and rest in Him. Some of my friends have been through great trials during pregnancy and God sustained them with His peace. As you read these testimonies, reflect on His words and promises to you.

Choose Life

by Allyson

God has been so good to us through the pregnancy and birth of all four of our children. When my first son, Josh, was born, the pregnancy was uneventful. The doctor induced me early, labor progressed, and about six hours later, I was holding a healthy baby in my arms. To our surprise, Josh was born with a severe club foot. One day after his birth, he was placed in a cast. This was the beginning of a trying season for me.

I had experienced healing in my life, had prayed for others and seen them healed, yet I prayed for Josh's foot and didn't see change. Many people agreed in prayer with us--still no supernatural instantaneous healing occurred. I questioned God about so many things. We pursued medical treatment and kept trusting God to take care of his foot. He spent many months in casts and has had two surgeries, but now he is able to run and play soccer and basketball. His healing didn't come the way I expected, but I know God was in the middle of the process. We learned that Tony, my husband, was himself born with two club feet, as was his natural father and his biological brothers. By prayer, we broke the curse of club feet from our family's lives and chose to trust God with our future.

Not long after that, I became pregnant with our daughter Corrie. This time, we didn't have insurance. We didn't qualify for assistance, but neither did we have the means to pay for a hospital delivery out of pocket. Not long after, I met a Christian midwife. She was a godsend. God blessed us with another uneventful pregnancy.

At the time, my husband, Tony, was driving a truck over the road for a living. With a midwife delivery, we were planning a homebirth and my desire was to have him there with me during our daughter's birth. My midwife and I came into a prayer of agreement that Corrie would be born when Tony was home. Each week, when he left, I would let her know when he would be gone and that I wasn't planning on calling her until he got back. God worked the timing out perfectly. I went into labor and delivered while Tony was home. God was my focal point during delivery. When the serious contractions came, I can remember praying for God to help me and give me strength during many of the contractions.

Corrie was a large baby at nine pounds, but we were blessed with an uneventful delivery and an easy recovery.

When Josh came in to see her for the first time, the first thing he did was look at her feet. They were perfect! No club feet this time. During this time, my husband's employer went through financial difficulties and several of his paychecks bounced. While a homebirth delivery with a midwife was substantially less than a hospital birth, with his work situation, the cost was still more than we had. The employer never reimbursed us for the bounced checks or paid Tony his lost wages, but the midwives blessed us by waiving a portion of the birth fee which just happened to equal the amount we were owed from his employer. What a blessing!

Caleb wasn't far behind Corrie. This time we had insurance, but elected to use the same midwife and plan for a homebirth, even though it wasn't covered by our insurance policy. This pregnancy was smooth and uneventful. When Caleb was born, we realized how God had protected him in my womb. His umbilical cord was forty-two inches long and had several knots in it that never tightened. When he was born, his lungs didn't clear well and he refused to cry despite various attempts to clear his lungs. We prayed over him and it wasn't much longer until he let out a good cry and finally cleared his lungs. Also, he was the first boy born since Josh. The club foot gene had always followed the boys. Caleb's feet were perfect; the curse was broken! Praise God!

After Caleb, we decided we were done having children. Still, after a few years, God began stirring in my heart that He wasn't finished. I was faced with a decision--would I let God have His way? I talked to Tony and we decided to leave it up to Him. About nine months later, we were expecting again. We considered a homebirth with a midwife again, but in my heart, I didn't have peace about that decision. We decided to go with the more traditional birth with an OB at the hospital.

I wasn't as young as I was with the first three children and this pregnancy was more difficult. It seemed that every test they did came back troublesome and I was monitored and poked much more than the previous pregnancies. Even though I had to modify my diet, log my meals, and measure my blood sugars throughout the day, Isaac was growing strong and healthy.

With a history of a big baby, my OB decided to induce early. Strapped to many monitors and attached to an IV, my labor progressed and Isaac's heartbeat remained strong. When it was time to deliver, Isaac came out with one big push. I don't think the doctor expected him that soon and he snatched him up and placed him hastily on my chest.

He was beautiful. We loved on him and admired him as any proud parent would. No crying…no breathing…quickly he was snatched away and hospital staff came running through the halls to work with him. At one point, one of the nurses, in a panic, shouted out that they were losing him. Immediately faith rose up in me. I stretched my hand toward him and declared, "No devil, you'll not steal my son from me. Isaac, you will not die but live and declare the works of the Lord." (Psalm 118:17.)

I believe in that instant, God touched his little body and healed him and within less than a minute he was stable, breathing, and doing great. Isaac doesn't have a club foot either. The pain medicine I was given during labor never took, but did leave me with an awful spinal headache. While I took medicine to deal with the headache, I was trusting God to heal the spinal leak causing them. The day before I would have had to go back in for a blood patch, they finally stopped. God healed my baby and restored me, too. What a blessing little Isaac has been to our family.

Every day, we are faced with challenges and trials. To experience God's blessing, I've learned to choose life. While standing in faith isn't easy, God's grace is always enough to get us though every situation. I pray that you too are stirred to not settle for whatever life throws at you, but to fight the good fight of faith to lay hold of all the promises God has for you.

> I shall not die, but live, and declare the works
> of the Lord. Psalm 118:17 KJV

Peace

by Leah

On a hot August day in 2009, I got up and went to work. I started to set up my brand new classroom. I was exactly 37 weeks pregnant and I worked in a school with no air conditioning. It was quite possibly in the 90 degree range inside of the school that day. Fun combination, no? I put up bulletin boards, made copies, got my textbooks, and finalized my maternity leave plans (because I knew Kade would be born sometime in the following weeks). At 2:30 P.M., I took one last look around my classroom, locked the door, and went downstairs to attend a faculty meeting. I had my 37 week doctor's appointment scheduled at 3:30 P.M.

I went to the doctor's appointment. The nurse took my blood pressure. She shook her head and called over another nurse, who took it again. She got someone else to take it to make sure that the first two nurses were correct. Then, they sent me to the hospital.

I have never been so scared in my life. I had never, ever, in my life been in the hospital as a patient. They said they were just going to monitor my blood pressure for a few hours and make sure I didn't have preeclampsia, but when they hooked me up to the monitor, they discovered I was having contractions. Big contractions. Fairly close contractions. So, they told me that they were going to keep me in the hospital, and that I would most likely have a baby in the next day or so. They broke my water, hooked me up to Pitocin, and we waited.

I was super nervous and scared. Not only was my life about to change, but my body was not cooperating with my blood pressure being high. I had wanted things to be perfect. But then, I was reminded of the importance of it all. And that was that this child, this baby, my little boy that I had already named Kade, was my gift from God and He had both of us in His hands. Then, I began to relax and to breathe a little deeper. After only 30 minutes of pushing, Kade was born at 12:15 A.M. the next morning and was perfectly healthy--and so was I. My blood pressure came back down into the normal range. God's peace sustained me that day.

...then you will experience god's peace, which exceeds anything we can understand. His peace will guard your hearts and minds as you live in Christ Jesus.
Philippians 4:7

He Never Failed Me

by Julie

In December 2002, I found out that after five years of marriage, my husband, Jeremy, and I were expecting our first baby. The first part of the pregnancy was filled with nausea, nausea, and more nausea. I couldn't find anything that sounded good. I was sick first thing in the morning, in the afternoon, and at night. Sleep was the only time that I wasn't nauseous. After getting through that first little rough patch, I felt pretty good for a few months. I was due to give birth in August and the Oklahoma heat during the summer is not very kind. Around the end of May and the first part of June, I started to feel really uncomfortable. The baby, whom we knew now was a boy and whom we named Jonah, was growing rapidly and so was I. My sister got married in June of that year and driving the 16 hours home and back was not very fun for a seven-month-pregnant body. After we got home from the trip, the pregnancy seemed to go downhill immediately.

I went back to work to find out that my insurance was changing July 1st. This brought some stress on me due to the financial aspect of knowing what I was expected to pay ahead of time to now being expected to pay almost triple of what we had first thought. I went to my next doctor's appointment and the receptionist had a hard time with processing the insurance change and I was feeling very overwhelmed. By the time I got back into the room with the doctor, my blood pressure was elevated. She laid me down on the table and checked the baby's heartbeat and some other things and then let me rest a bit. She checked my blood pressure again and it had lowered, so I was able to go home.

Still feeling very anxious and uncomfortable from a huge baby, I went home and tried to relax. I had noticed that I was beginning to swell daily in my ankles. The heat wasn't helping either. I just felt awful and spent most of my time in the recliner. A few weeks later, my feet and legs were so swollen that I couldn't put any kind of pants or shoes on. I had to wear shorts or skirts to work. The doctor was concerned and told me that she recommended that I take off work at this time. Reluctantly, I agreed to work a week and a half more and then start my maternity leave.

I could hardly walk around by the afternoon because of my feet and legs. My husband was working nights and I slept very little. I felt very discouraged and a little depressed. Was this how pregnancy was supposed to be? I remember walking across the parking lot and into work in the August heat on my last day and thinking I didn't know if I could go another step. My parents had been in town a few weeks earlier and had to go buy me open-toed shoes in two sizes larger than normal to fit on my feet. Even those shoes were becoming tight.

I somehow finished out my last day and went home that night. I was keeping track of my blood pressure at home. Most of every day and night was spent in the recliner trying to get the swelling to go down. My sister, Sara, had asked for vacation immediately when she found out my due date. She was going to be with me for one week. I had been praying that the Lord would work out the timing so that Jonah would be born when my family was around, since both sets of our families lived out of state.

Sara had arrived on Sunday – the beginning of my 39th week of pregnancy. The morning of my 39 week appointment, on a Wednesday, I took my blood pressure and it was up quite a bit. I didn't really feel any different. I hadn't felt good in months, so it was hard to know good from bad anymore. When I got to the doctor, the nurse took my blood pressure and said it was 170/100. At the beginning of the pregnancy, it was running 100/65. The doctor came in and took it again and it was still as high. She said, "Well we are going to have a baby today." I was so happy that this would finally be over, and most of all, that I would see my precious baby.

We went over to the hospital. Sara called Mom and Dad and Jeremy called his parents. His parents, sister, and nephew were able to arrive by dinner that evening and my parents and brother were on their way as well. It was important to me that my family be there and God didn't disappoint. The doctor had me hooked up to Pitocin but it caused the contractions to be too close together and not strong enough. About 1 A.M. that morning, the nurse told me that my doctor was coming in to break my water. She broke my water and I tried to rest a little. I had decided on an epidural and was resting pretty comfortably at that point.

About 3 A.M., the doctor came to check on my progress. I was only dilated to about a six and when she checked my catheter, I didn't have any urine coming out. She was concerned, because of my high blood pressure, that my kidneys were starting to shut down and all that fluid had to go somewhere. She worked on the catheter for awhile and decided that if I had not produced any urine by 5 A.M., we were going to do a C-section. They stopped the Pitocin as well at this time.

At this point, I was too tired to care. I just wanted this baby out and for my body to not fail me. At 5 A.M., my parents and brother walked through the door. My dad prayed and commanded my kidneys to start working in Jesus' name. The nurse came in and I had started to feel incredible pressure in my legs. I told the nurse and she repositioned me and pushed the epidural IV for more medicine. I didn't get any relief and so she came in again and decided to check my progress. She said, "Timing is everything! We're at a 10!" She also let me know that I had produced some urine.

I felt so thankful , knowing that the Lord had His hand in all of this. Jonah was born at 6:48 A.M. and weighed 9 lbs 12oz. God worked out all of what I had been concerned about. My heart's desire that my family be in town was granted and momma and baby were healthy. He is faithful!

The LORD will perfect that which concerns me;
your mercy, O LORD, endures forever
Psalm 138:8 NKJV

Faith and a Red Bag

by Ninkey

How a red bag can change a person's life is way beyond my understanding, but I know it happened. I suppose, or rather, I believe, everything's possible if we believe.

The couple was young, married only a few, very happy years. They began to talk about, and dream about, a family. A year passed by and two. During the third year, they became quite concerned about not conceiving a child and as of the couple's fourth year waiting and praying, they decided to consult a physician. From this point on, another three years found the couple constantly tossed about from appointment to appointment, month to month, disappointment to frustration, waging a battle with infertility.

The couple lived, loved, worked, and continued to dream, despite discouraging reports. With the help of family and friends, they kept faith that one day, their hearts' desire would be granted. She had one very special friend, a co-worker named Kathy, who always listened, sharing tears and words of faith. The friend came to work one morning and presented the young woman with a gift. It was a large red bag whose front bore the words, "World's Greatest Baby". Smiling, the friend explained that the gift was to be a constant reminder that a child would be forthcoming, and each time the young woman looked at it, she should be encouraged that "faith is the substance of things hoped for, the evidence of things unseen."

The special gift was received by the young woman with tears of gratitude. It was taken home and shared with her husband. Together, the couple hung the bag where they could see it. Among the many ways their faith was fed, the red bag became a daily visible symbol of hope. Although little had changed about the medical aspects, much had changed as the young couple believed that God wanted to give them a family.

Early one spring, in the seventh year of their marriage, the woman received a phone call. Her physician was calling to say that all he knew to do had been done, but chances were minute for their being parents. The couple felt the impact of his words, but continued to hold onto a hope that had been sown, watered, and nurtured in their hearts for a while now.

Summer ended, and the couple celebrated a seventh anniversary. Seven is the number of perfection, some say, and they felt that it expressed their feelings about life to this point except for their lack of children. They filled the void by spending time with a group of teenagers and doting on nieces and nephews.

Life continued to be good to them, but the husband grew concerned about his wife. Her job was very demanding and he returned home often to find her stretched out and resting on the couch. The day she called him, he sensed the obvious effort she was making to keep her voice normal sounding. The news hit him hard, threatening to take him off his feet. Could she be telling him the truth? Was this a cruel joke?

The eighth anniversary (yes, eight is the number of completion) found the couple parents of a wonderful, beautiful baby girl. The family they had longed, prayed, and trusted God for was here! There was no way to describe the joy they experienced at her birth and miraculous first moments in the world.

The mother and father knew this story would be held close and told to their daughter as she grew up. And it was. Maybe she would find hope and purpose in life because of it.

As for the red diaper bag, it continued to hang as a reminder that "faith is the substance of things hoped for, the evidence of things unseen."

Now faith is the substance of things hoped for,
the evidence of things not seen.
Hebrews 11:1 NKJV

His Promises are Yes and Amen!

by Nancy

When I was pregnant with my first child, Christina, I planned to have the birth as natural as possible. Several things went wrong. First, my doctor, who was a Christian, was not available when I went into labor. The doctor that I had to use was known as the abortion doctor in town. Then, Christina was in breech, "butt first," position. I signed the hospital form as "No Spinal," but was given one anyway while I got a C-section. They used forceps on her which I had not agreed to.

But through all of that, we were so blessed to have our beautiful daughter, Christina. We thanked God for her.

For our next child, I decided to trust God for a super-natural birth without any interventions that we did not want. I was told that a vaginal birth might be dangerous, but I did extensive research and felt safe in having my next baby at home. I found an experienced midwife that I used during the entire nine months. Also, a nurse that we knew from church came to our home for the birth.

I prayed and trusted God and I refused to fear. I felt God's design for childbirth was a miracle and a blessing, not a disease or sickness. Having a baby to me was as natural as breathing.

It was late Halloween night, October 31, when the labor pains started. They were mild, like menstrual cramps. I prayed, "Lord please let this baby be born November 1 and not on Halloween."

I stayed on my feet, walking and working with the contractions and gravity. From the first discomfort to the birth, it was 2 ½ hours. I did not take any pain relievers, not even something over the counter. The great thing was that I did not need anything for pain. I kept my focus on God and His promises--Psalm 91, Psalm 118:8, Proverbs 3:5-6.

As the time came for Jeremy to be born, I didn't talk; I only said the name of Jesus three times. He was born on November 1.

It was a divine natural occurrence. I trusted God and I give Him all the glory for a safe, peaceful and joyful experience and a healthy, brilliant baby boy. He is now 25 years old and healthy.

> For all the promises of God in Him are Yes, and in Him Amen, to the glory of God through us.
> 2 Corinthians 1:20 NKJV

Psalm 34:7

by Brenda

This was a verse I stood upon when I thought I would never live my dream of having kids. All my life, all I ever wanted was to be a mommy! According to doctors, that wouldn't happen. I had stage 4 endometriosis with PCOS (Polycystic Ovaries). As a result, my tubes were severely damaged. I am so thankful that God has the last say. After four years of trying, I finally gave birth to a son, Braden Scott, on February 16, 2007.

After several months went by, we decided to try again, and to our surprise, got pregnant right away. We couldn't wait to find out what we were having! At 17 weeks along, in the beginning of November, we had our ultrasound scheduled. I remember how exciting it was to see Braden on the monitor for the first time and I couldn't wait! During the scan, I remember thinking, *Why is this taking so long? It didn't take this long last time.* I thought nothing of it when she told us we were having a little girl. My husband, Jason, and I, were so excited! We already had her name picked out--Jacee Dawn.

As our ultrasound continued, again, I wondered why this was taking forever. I tried to ignore it and just kept trying to be excited that we were having a little girl. It was finally over so she sent us out to the waiting room until our doctor was ready for my check-up. I kept having an uneasy feeling, even while looking at our pictures, but I didn't really know why.

Now, waiting in the exam room for our doctor, I was excited, yet worried, at the same time. I just wanted her to come in, tell us everything looked great, and send us on our way. Well....that's not what happened at all. She came in and started going over the results of the scan. I now knew why I had that uneasy feeling. She said that our little girl wasn't growing like she should and even if she made it full term, her little body wouldn't be compatible with life. Wow! I felt as though the breath had been knocked out of me. They wanted to do more testing to find out what was going on. All I could think at the time was, *I'm not losing my little girl!* So...we agreed to have some tests done.

On our way home, we made some phone calls so our family would be in prayer with us. All we could do over the next couple of days was pray and wait to hear what the test revealed. Two, very long, agonizing days later, the call came.

Jacee had a very rare condition known as triploidy (instead of two sets of chromosomes in her DNA, she had three; that translates as developmental information overload).

We were given the option of terminating the pregnancy, but quickly refused. We knew, as it says in Luke 1:37, that nothing is impossible with God. We were told that Jacee wouldn't make it another month. We had to go back in to the doctor's office every week to make sure there was still a heartbeat. A month came and went and I could still feel her moving around, and her heartbeat was strong. My hopes were up, so I continued to pray that God would heal my little girl.

After another month and a half went by, I went into labor. I was only 7 months along. Even while giving birth, there was still a part of me hoping and praying Jacee would be okay. On January 21, 2008, Martin Luther King Day, our Jacee Dawn was born, stillborn. Our world had fallen apart. We were allowed to spend as much time with her as we wanted. After several hours went by, it was hard to let her go, but we knew she wasn't sick anymore. She was with Jesus. It hurt to say goodbye. I knew she had been alive, because I had felt her kicks, her hiccups. Now they were gone, and I had to rely on God to get me through.

We left the hospital without our baby girl, only to go home and prepare her funeral. Proverbs 3:5 says to trust in the Lord with all your heart and lean not on your own understanding. I didn't understand. Things just didn't make sense! I could ask, "Why?" all day long, but I'd never get an answer that would satisfy me. I had to just trust Him to see me through this. It wasn't easy, but it would've been a whole lot worse without my Jesus! Even though my experience wasn't as I had prayed, His Word never changed and He is faithful!

We went on to have another little boy on January 19, 2009. Bryce Randall was born on Martin Luther King Day, exactly one year later. We got to bring him home on January 21, the one year anniversary of our losing Jacee. Only God could've planned that. He is so amazing!

Our nest wasn't quite complete yet. We knew we wanted another child. We found out we were expecting again in November of 2009. Excited again, we couldn't wait to find out the sex. On one hand, we would love to have a girl – on the other, the thought scared me. I felt, as Jacee's mom, that I didn't do my part to take care of her, so why would this time be any different? I know that was Satan trying to discourage me. Isaiah 41:10 says do not fear, for the Lord is with us. I knew God was taking care of me and our new little one. So, although a little nervous, we went for our ultrasound. We were having a girl! Knowing our worries, our doctor assured us that everything looked normal and she was growing just as she should be. Thank You, Lord! We went on to have a normal, healthy pregnancy.

On July 21, 2010, Jalyn Dawn, was born. Everything was going great, until later that night. The nurses brought her in so I could feed her. She didn't seem to want to eat, she wanted to sleep, so we decided we would try again later. They brought her back around two that morning. This time, she ate some, but started spitting up. My concern with that was that thespit up was green. It didn't seem normal to me. I called the nurses and explained to them what was going on. They took Jalyn down for some tests to be run. Scared, I asked God to be with her.

They brought her back around 5 A.M., and said her white blood cell count was low, but she would be fine. Thinking all was well, I tried to feed her again. The spitting up became more throwing up, so I called the nurse back in. They took her so they could monitor her, only to find that she continued throwing up. Knowing it had to be more than her blood count, they ran more tests. This time, they found she had malrotation (a twisting of the intestines, or bowel that caused obstruction). Surgery was needed. At twenty-three hours old, Jalyn went in for surgery. Trying to be strong, I prayed for my little girl. The surgery went well. She stayed in the NICU for two weeks, recovering. Finally able to take her home, we knew God had His hand on her. Once home, she started eating better, growing, and was able to keep her food down. Life was good! We had our three kids, they were healthy, and all was well!

On November 14, 2010, our lives were getting ready to be shaken, again. Our doctors had advised us that if Jalyn ever threw up anything green, to take her to the emergency room. That night, before bed, she threw up her bottle, but it wasn't green. We were thankful, but still concerned, because she had never done that before. I decided to sleep near her, so I could keep an eye on her. She threw up a little more before going to sleep. Still nothing green, but I wondered if I should call the doctor. She slept well, but early the next morning, she threw up after her bottle. This time it was green. Scared, we took her to the emergency room. They admitted us pretty quickly and began a series of tests. The surgeon came in that night and said that they didn't find any blockage and he wouldn't need to see her again, that she would be fine in a day or two. We thought that was great news. The only problem is that days went on with no change. She was still throwing up.

Doctors didn't know what was going on. They ran test after test, still not finding anything major. They thought it was a virus at first, and then thought it was reflux. As her mom, I knew that wasn't it, but how do you argue with doctors?

After ten long, very frustrating days with no answers, they sent us home, still thinking it was reflux. They thought she would be better in a couple of days, but she continued to throw up. Our question, though, was why was it still green? Why was it so urgent for us to get her to the emergency room? Surely, with it being green, with her history, and them advising us to get her in if her vomit was ever green, they had to know something else was going on.

We went home the day before Thanksgiving. Jalyn would eat every now and then but would still throw up. Sometimes a little, other times quite a bit. We were worried she would get dehydrated. She was having wet diapers, though, so we just continued to keep an eye on her, knowing that not producing wet diapers was a sign of dehydration. She started throwing up quite a bit more and all of a sudden just didn't look well. Very scared, and to be honest, mad, we rushed her back to the emergency room on Thanksgiving Day. She was severely dehydrated.

They got her hooked up to an IV and admitted us right away. After some blood work was done, they thought they found that she had pyloric stenosis (a tightening in the pyloric muscle just after the stomach that doesn't allow food to pass). She needed surgery….again. We were then told that she would have to be transported to Oklahoma City because there were no longer any pediatric surgeons in Tulsa. Wow… really? My patience was wearing thin. I wanted my daughter well.

Now we had to wait and find a surgeon who would take her. *Lord, please open the door to the right one!* The surgeon we found wanted more testing done because the first diagnosis didn't make sense to him-not with her age and the fact that what she was throwing up was green. The radiologist at our current hospital refused to do more x-rays. My flesh really wanted to lay in to some doctors! I had to ask for God's help because I was getting ready to lose it. I was running on very little sleep and I was missing my family. I was very emotional. I let them know how frustrated I was. We all know, as moms, that no one messes with our babies! Here my little girl was sick and no one seemed to want to help her.

Finally, the day after Thanksgiving, we were transported, by ambulance to Oklahoma City. Shortly after arriving, the surgeon came in and met with us. After viewing Jalyn's x-rays himself, he decided surgery was definitely needed. It was scheduled for the next morning, around 8 A.M. My baby girl, at four months old, was being prepared for her second surgery. *Lord, I need Your peace that Jalyn's going to be alright. You said fear not, for You are with us.*

Jalyn came through surgery just fine. The doctors confirmed more malrotation (and not pyloric stenosis). We were so frustrated, but also thankful that they were finally able to find the problem and correct it. Why couldn't they find this on the x-rays two weeks earlier? Now we had to wait for her to recover. Tired of being in hospitals, wanting my husband and my boys with me, my trust was in God, yet again.

Jalyn's surgery took place on a Saturday. By that following Tuesday, I was really having a hard time. I hadn't seen my boys since Thanksgiving Day and I was missing them terribly. Sissy was still recovering. She had to be able to go the bathroom on her own before we could take her home. She was on morphine and Tylenol to keep her comfortable. That night, Satan was doing his best to attack me. He kept trying to tell me, "Remember, you couldn't take care of Jacee....now look at your Jalyn." I was fighting pretty hard that night, not knowing what was getting ready to come.

The next morning, around 5:30, the nurse came in to give Jalyn morphine. She hadn't had any since the night before and she was getting pretty uncomfortable. Friends had told us vaguely of the danger of administering morphine to children so young, but we trusted the doctors. At 6 A.M., however, her monitors were going pretty crazy. I went over to check on her as a nurse was coming in. Jalyn was not responsive. She was laying on her right side and all I can remember as the nurse turned her to her back, was a blue, lifeless little girl.

I couldn't breathe! This was not happening! As I grabbed my phone to call my husband, all I could do was pray. I was screaming and praying for her to live and not die. When I couldn't say anything else, all I could say was, "Jesus, Jesus, Jesus!" That name is so powerful! It was only when I said His name that I could keep myself calm. A Code Blue was called and doctors from all over the hospital rushed in her room in a matter of seconds. After five minutes of CPR, I was told she was going to be moved to ICU....they had a pulse.

All of a sudden, we heard a cry! It was her! She was given a narcotics reversal and within a minute, she was fine! The shot countered the effects of the morphine, which had stopped her breathing and ultimately, her heart. And she also had a full diaper! Thank you, Jesus! All I could do was look at her, talk to her, and cry. I couldn't say, "Thank you Jesus!" enough. He had revived her.

I couldn't wait for my husband to walk through the door. I was emotionally and physically drained. I was finally allowed to hold Jalyn. I knew God had touched her. In the days to follow, we found out that several family members and one of our board members from our church, had been praying pretty hard. God laid us on their hearts before they knew anything was going on. God knew and He used our loved ones to intercede. When God lays someone on your heart, please pray for them. You never know what they're going through. You don't have to know the details....God knows. Just listen to Him. It could be you one day who needs the prayer. You would want to know that if God laid you on my heart so strongly, that I would pray for you.

No matter what you may be going through, know that there are people who care about you. Jesus cares about you and what you are going through. He knew my desire to be a mom. He knows yours, too. He loves you and is always right there with you! I promise, He can get you through anything. So many things I've gone through, I thought I'd never make it. But I look back on my life now and see Jesus every step of the way. Don't give up....remember the "Footprints" poem: "It was then that I was carrying you."

We were released from the hospital on that following Saturday. A miracle! We were going home. Jalyn is now a healthy toddler and is doing great! She is the happiest baby I've ever seen. Even while in the hospital, sick and going through tests, she always had the biggest smile on her face, a lesson for us all. I thank my family and my church for all of their prayers. All of my babies are miracles. I was told I would never have them. Satan tried to take my Jalyn, but all I have to say is watch out....she's gonna do great things for our God!

Your mercy, O LORD, is in the heavens;
Your faithfulness reaches to the clouds.
Psalm 36:5 NKJV

Congratulations...
You are Pregnant!

You are probably just finding this out and you are already four weeks along. Pretty good deal, huh? You might be experiencing some conflicting emotions – happy one second and sad the next. One minute you might be excited and another minute overwhelmed. That is part of the whole pregnancy journey. No matter what you are feeling, don't feel guilty about it. Condemning yourself is not the work of our heavenly Father. He tells us in Romans 8:1 that there is no condemnation for those who are in Christ Jesus. This pregnancy, whether planned or unplanned, is a gift from God. He is by your side every step of the way and not one circumstance catches Him off guard.

I have known pregnant women who have tracked each cycle and known their exact fertile times and women who found themselves pregnant when they had done everything to prevent it. In the end, the result is the same – a sweet gift from heaven.

The Word of God is rich and will provide you everything that you need for this journey. His joy is your strength (Nehemiah 8:10). When you feel that there are times that you can't go on, reflect on the scriptures provided in this devotional and draw strength from Him. When you feel so happy that you could dance, praise the Lord and thank Him for what He has done for you.

The Sovereign LORD is my strength! He makes me as surefooted as a deer, able to tread upon the heights.
Habakkuk 3:19

But God, This Is Not What I Had Planned...

by Chrissy

My husband and I felt our family was now complete. We had our boy and our girl. I was over 35 and had gone through a miscarriage and two C-sections and felt like we had been blessed enough. Our precious baby girl, Annie Elizabeth, was three weeks old when my husband had a vasectomy in September of 2009. I was breastfeeding Annie and my cycle had returned only once, but I was not too concerned because of breastfeeding. I was not losing the weight from the pregnancy. I even asked my mom about not losing weight after a girl. I began thinking that I might have a uterine tumor.

So, then, my husband Mark and I decided to start working out. We bought the Insanity workout DVD's. We were working out every evening. I began losing weight, but my stomach began looking bigger. I made comments that I thought I looked pregnant, but knew that it was impossible, because Mark had been "fixed".

Around the end of June 2010, I felt the feeling that I will never forget. I felt a kick. I immediately called my husband at work in tears and with fear in my heart. Of course, being a teacher/mother was demanding enough and the thoughts of having another child were overwhelming! This is not what I had planned at all!

Mark was on break at his job when he received the call from me. Mark, in his normal "calm down mode," began trying to comfort me, but nothing could bring peace to me. He went and spoke with his supervisor and told him he needed to leave early. On the way home, Mark stopped at CVS Pharmacy and purchased a pregnancy test. When he returned home, I was in tears.

As the pregnancy test hit the kitchen table, it was like the moment before the last second passes to win The Super Bowl. It was a feeling of dread, fear, excitement, and disbelief. Could this really be happening to me? Mark and I prayed and held hands before the test began. Mark said something like," Your will be done," and off to the bathroom I went with test strip in hand. Moments later, I exited the bathroom and my chest and head felt like they were in a vice. My mouth went dry and tears of sadness ran down my face. Mark knew in a second that I was pregnant and there was nothing we could do to change it. I had so many negative thoughts and emotions rise up within me. I didn't know if I wanted this baby. I wanted to run away, but quickly realized the enemy was speaking to me. These were all selfish thoughts about me, me, me.

I scheduled an appointment with my OB/GYN. The doctor that had delivered my first two children had retired, and I was scared and unsure about the new doctor. My first visit was amazing. My new doctor said, "This baby was meant to be." He stated that God had a plan for this life. I knew from that point on that God had a plan for this baby, as well as for me. I began to have peace and know that God had His hand on me and this precious child.

I knew that I was pretty far along, but did not know exactly. He estimated by ultrasound that I was around 5 ½ months pregnant. My due date would be around the first part of November.

The rest of the pregnancy went as planned and I did not have any complications. Ben Wesley Hurley arrived on November 2, 2010, Election Day, through C-section. He is the most beautiful little gift. He has blessed our family with such joy, and we are so thankful that our God intervened even when I thought I had it all planned out.

> The mind of man plans his way,
> but the LORD directs his steps.
> Proverbs 16:9 NASB

In His Time...

by Jennifer

Two years after being married, my husband and I felt that we were ready to have a baby and began trying to become pregnant. I had been on birth control and was sure I would get pregnant the first time we tried. It didn't happen like that for us. My husband and I tried for a couple of years to get pregnant. It was the worst time in my life, thinking each month that I could be pregnant and then always being disappointed. I prayed and tried to trust in God, but each month that went by made me more faithless. My friends and family did not stop praying, though. They had faith for me when I was weak.

After a couple of years, I found out I was pregnant. My hopes were high and I was terribly disappointed when I went in for my twelve week appointment and saw that the baby's heart had stopped beating. I felt like God had given up on me. I was afraid I would never have children. I remember talking to God one night and saying, "You need to give me a sign if You are hearing me." A few minutes later, I was organizing some things downstairs in my home and found a little ceramic figure my aunt had made me when I was a little girl. The figure was praying hands with a little girl inside the hands. The inscription said, "See, I have not forgotten you. I have you carved on the palm of my hand." (Isaiah 49:15.) It took my breath away. God spoke to me in the manner that he had spoken to Gideon. He gave me a sign and renewed my faith.

Soon after, God spoke to a man from my church and told him I would have a son. He stepped out in faith and announced what God had told him to the congregation. Two other pastors (that did not hear this man's testimony) also said God told them I would have a son. Two months later, I was pregnant! God gave me my first child in January, 2004. God gave me a son.

I now have four beautiful children. Although waiting on a child was one of the most difficult times in my life, I am grateful to God for that time. I may not have been as appreciative of my children if I had not gone through that time of waiting. I remember my grandfather's favorite verse, "They that wait upon the LORD shall renew their strength; they shall mount up with wings as eagles; they shall run and not grow weary, they shall walk and not faint" (Isaiah 40:31 KJV).

See, I have written your name on the
palms of my hands.
Isaiah 49:15

God's Gift

by Jenn

After 17 years of health issues and doctors not believing I could carry a baby, I found myself staring at a positive pregnancy test one August morning in 2008. *Wow – how could this be?* I was excited, of course, but nervous beyond belief. My husband was speechless. We decided to make an appointment with a reputable doctor in town that had been in practice for many years.

When it came time for my appointment at about 6 weeks pregnant, I was so anxious I could hardly contain myself. After all the paperwork and the routine blood work, etc., was done, the doctor came in with a very grave face. He told me that he believed that I had a molar pregnancy. My blood work was showing that I was further along than I really should be and he couldn't see any baby on an ultrasound yet. I was terrified and began to cry. In my heart, I screamed out to God, "How is this happening? I have longed for this child for so many years and now this?"

Because it was the Friday before Labor Day, I had to wait until Tuesday to go in and get a D&C at the hospital. He scheduled me for that Tuesday morning around 9:00 A.M. I remember going home and crying so hard that I couldn't even contain myself from shaking. My husband and one of my best friends were convinced, however, that this doctor was wrong. It was hard not to doubt but I started to remember the scriptures I had read and the prayers I had prayed, knowing that God wanted me to have the desire of my heart, which was to be a mother.

Tuesday morning came and we went to the hospital. When I got into the room for the ultrasound to confirm that there was no baby, I was completely surprised and overwhelmed when the ultrasound tech said, "There's a baby and a heartbeat!" Tears of joy ran down my face and when I looked to my husband, he was crying as well. It was a miracle!

Seven months later on April 3, 2009, I gave birth to a beautiful baby girl, who is our gift from heaven.

For the word of the LORD holds true,
and we can trust everything he does.
Psalm 33:4

Early Pregnancy Symptoms

Some women say that they began experiencing pregnancy symptoms as early as a couple of days after conception. Others say that they never really felt much different at all. Both can be normal. Here's a list of some common (and not so common) early pregnancy symptoms:

- Extreme fatigue
- Sore breasts
- Unusual hunger and thirst
- Mood swings
- Nausea
- Sensitive gums
- Forgetfulness
- Increased urination
- Excess bloating and gas
- Vivid dreams
- Heightened sense of smell
- Implantation bleeding
- Absence of period

How Your Baby is Growing

Implantation is typically occurring around this time. The embryo, which is now called a blastocyst, looks for a place to implant inside the uterus. The embryonic period begins this week, meaning that from now until 10 weeks, all of your baby's organs will start to develop and some of them will even start working during this time. Your baby sort of looks like a little sea creature with a tail.

How Your Life is Changing

You may be feeling just a little "off" or not right, or you might not be feeling a thing. Some women don't have nausea for a few more weeks, but you might be feeling a little nauseated. You probably are feeling really tired, too, but that just means your body is working very hard right now. Your breasts might also start to feel very tender.

For more early pregnancy symptoms, check out page 79.

What the Word Says

The LORD is my strength and shield. I trust him, and he helps me. I am very happy, and I praise him with my song.

Psalm 28:7 NCV

It is God who arms me with strength and keeps my way secure.

Psalm 18:32 NIV

This Week's Confession of Faith

Father, just as Your Word says, I will trust in You and You will help me. I ask for Your help during this pregnancy. You be my guide, my strength, and my happiness. **I commit this pregnancy to You.**

Thank You, Father, that You are my strength. You surround me with everything that I need. You keep my way secure and are my shield. Even though I may feel exhausted, I know that You will get me through!

How Your Baby is Growing

Baby is the size of a sesame seed. He looks like a tiny tadpole. His neural tube, which sprouts the brain, spinal cord, backbone, and nerves, is beginning to form.

Already, during this week, his heart divides into chambers and begins to beat and pump blood.

His head is growing much faster than the rest of his body right now. His brain is changing in order to regulate heart rate, blood circulation, and other functions.

How Your Life is Changing

Your symptoms are probably starting to be stronger. Morning sickness may be starting to kick in and your areolas on your breasts are darkening due to hormones.

You are most likely starting to feel really tired, so rest whenever you can.

If you haven't already, you should probably call and get a doctor's appointment scheduled for the routine first visit, which includes a full health history and blood work.

What the Word Says

No wonder my heart is glad, and I rejoice. My body rests in safety.

Psalm 16:9

Trust in the LORD with all your heart; do not depend on your own understanding.

Proverbs 3:5

This Week's Confession of Faith

Thank you, Father, for this life inside of me. Even though he is small, he is still alive and my heart is happy for that reason. I pray that as his heart begins to beat, that it will be strong physically and sensitive to Your voice all the days of his life. In Jesus' name, amen.

I put my whole trust in You, Lord. You won't let me down. As I go to my doctor soon, I thank You for giving my doctor wisdom and compassion for me so that I will get the best care possible. Thank You for Your hand upon me and my baby.

How Your Baby is Growing

The nose, mouth, and ears that you'll spend so much time kissing are beginning to take shape. His head becomes more distinct with tiny spots appearing that mark the places where his eyes will form. Spots for his ears also become visible. Buds that will later become arms and legs begin. His heart is beating about 100 to 160 times a minute — almost twice as fast as yours — and blood is beginning to course through his body. His intestines are developing, and the bud of tissue that will give rise to his lungs has appeared. Right now, your baby is a quarter of an inch long, about the size of a pea.

How Your Life is Changing

You may be feeling tired and moody, even sad sometimes. You also may be experiencing some nausea most commonly referred to as "morning sickness".

During the first trimester, the fear of a threatened miscarriage is sometimes hard to shake. Try not to worry too much. It isn't good for you or your baby.

What the Word Says

Don't be sad, because the joy of the LORD will make you strong.

Nehemiah 8:10 NCV

And I will rebuke the devourer for your sakes, and he shall not destroy the fruits of your ground; neither shall your vine cast her fruit before the time in the field.

Malachi 3:11 KJV

This Week's Confession of Faith

Thank you, Lord, for Your joy. You have entrusted me with this child and I will have joy no matter how I feel. By focusing on You and what You have done for me, all the bad fades away. I don't want to be sad, but I want to be joyful because of Your love for me.

Father, I pray blessings over this sweet baby. I know that Your desire is that I carry this baby healthy and whole to full-term. I speak that out in Jesus' name. I want Your desire, too. Help me to "let go" and trust in You through this journey. I love you, Father.

How Your Baby is Growing

The hands and feet are emerging this week from the developing arms and legs. They resemble little paddles. Your baby is technically still an embryo and has a small tail which is just an extension of his tailbone. It will disappear in a few weeks.

He has doubled in size since last week and measures about half an inch long, about the size of a blackberry. His eyelids are partially covering his eyes which already have a little bit of color. The circulatory system also becomes more complex as lungs begin to form.

How Your Life is Changing

You might be craving a certain food. One theory is that pregnancy cravings may be the body's way of getting the nutrients it needs.

You also may be visiting the bathroom more than normal thanks to your increasing blood volume and the extra fluid being processed through your kidneys.

What the Word Says

You must serve only the LORD your God. If you do, I will bless you with food and water and I will protect you from illness.

Exodus 23:25

"I say this because I know what I am planning for you," says the LORD. "I have good plans for you, not plans to hurt you. I will give you hope and a good future."

Jeremiah 29:11 NCV

This Week's Confession of Faith

Thank you, Father, that Your Word says that You know what You are planning for me and it is good. This child is part of Your good plan for me.

I speak to my baby's little hands and feet that are developing this week and I say that they will develop just as they are supposed to. I declare that my baby will use his hands and feet to spread the good news of the Gospel and help to win many to the Lord.

How Your Baby is Growing

This week, your baby is looking more like a miniature baby-to-be. Her cute little nose is beginning to protrude and her upper lip is taking shape.

Breathing tubes extend from her throat to the branches of her developing lungs. She is about the size of a kidney bean at just over a half an inch long.

Even though you can't feel her, she is constantly moving and shifting around.

How Your Life is Changing

You may notice that your bra is getting tighter. Rising levels of hormones can cause breast growth and other changes.

Because of the dramatic rise in progesterone, you may feel extra tired or sluggish.

Your abdomen will most likely be sore as well with all the growing and changing in your uterus.

What the Word Says

He fills my lifewith good things. My youth is re-newed like the eagle's!

Psalm 103:5

But those who trust in the LORD will find new strength. They will soar high on wings like eagles. They will run and not grow weary. They will walk and not faint.

Isaiah 40:31

This Week's Confession of Faith

Thank you, Lord, that You are continuing to watch over my child as she develops, from her lungs to that cute little nose. I speak to my child's lungs, that they be strong and shout out Your promises of goodness and love.

Father, thank You that You give me strength even when I feel tired and sluggish. I will have strength like the eagle!

How Your Baby is Growing

This week, sweet little baby is the size of an olive. He is starting to look more human. All of his essential body parts are accounted for.

The four chambers and valves of the heart start to form, as do his teeth. His eyes are fully formed, but his eyelids are fused shut and won't open until the third trimester.

How Your Life is Changing

Your body may need to relax and work on growing a baby. If you can, add more sleeping time to your day. You may want to invest in a good pregnancy sleep pillow or body pillow. If you are an exercise mommy, it might be good to do less strenuous workouts like swimming or Pilates (they even have Pilates for pregnancy).

A warm bath can also help, but just remember to avoid hot tubs due to the risk of the high temperatures. Don't give in to being stressed or restless. Our heavenly Father promises to take care of you!

What the Word Says

I go to bed and sleep in peace, because, LORD, only you keep me safe.

Psalm 4:8 NCV

You can go to bed without fear; you will lie down and sleep soundly.

Proverbs 3:24

This Week's Confession of Faith

Thank you, Father, for the sweet little baby in my womb. As her heart fully develops, I thank You that her heart will be Yours and Yours alone. Although her eyes are closed now, I pray that she will always look to You for her answers.

I praise You, Lord, that You promise in Your Word that my sleep can be peaceful. I take this promise that You have given me and rest in it this week and in all the weeks to come. Thank You for Your precious, sweet sleep that You give to me.

How Your Baby is Growing

Little one is the size of a red grape now. Most of his critical development is now complete.

This is also the beginning of the fetal period. He is no longer an embryo, but now a fetus! He can swallow fluid and kick.

The major organs, such as the kidneys, intestines, brain, and liver are all in place and starting to function! You may be able to see tiny nails on the fingers and toes and a little bit of peach fuzz growing on his skin.

How Your Life is Changing

Some women start to feel better around week ten. The hormones begin to level off and some of the early pregnancy symptoms begin to fade. This week your uterus is about the size of a grapefruit (it started out the size of a pear).

As your body prepares itself for the delivery of the baby, a hormone called relaxin is released. This hormone helps loosen and stretch the ligaments. Sometimes, women feel the stretching and pulling in the ligament areas. Just as the hormone's name reflects, try to relax and not worry. If the pain is severe, a call to the doctor might put you at ease.

What the Word Says

Let my soul be at rest again, for the LORD has been good to me.

Psalm 116:7

Come to me, all of you who are tired and have heavy loads, and I will give you rest.

Matthew 11:28 NCV

This Week's Confession of Faith

I praise You, Father, that my baby has all of his vital organs and that You have seen his development thus far and will continue to watch over him. I pray that as his organs begin to function that they will work exactly as You have created them to work, because You make no mistakes. I rest in the fact that I can trust You with my sweet baby.

I thank You, Lord, that You also desire for my soul to be at rest. I speak to my body to relax in Jesus' name and rest in Your perfect promises for me.

How Your Baby is Growing

Sweet little baby is about the size of a fig now. Her diaphragm is developing and she may start to have hiccups.

Her head is really big, but that will even out as she grows. She may look a little strange now because of her big head, but she is still swimming around and stretching and moving effortlessly.

How Your Life is Changing

Last week, we mentioned the hormones in the body causing relaxation in the ligaments and the same is true for the valve between the stomach and esophagus, which can cause heartburn.

A good remedy for this is to eat small, healthy meals and snacks more frequently.

What the Word Says

You saw my bones being formed as I took shape in my mother's body. When I was put together there, you saw my body as it was formed.

Psalm 139:15-16 NCV

I, the LORD, will watch over it, watering it carefully. Day and night I will watch so no one can harm it.

Isaiah 27:3

This Week's Confession of Faith

Father, I praise You that this miracle of life inside of me is alive and moving. Even though I can't see her, You always can. Thank You for Your protection that You have promised for me and my family.

Lord, thank You that I can relax in knowing that You watch over my baby. In Your Word, You tell me that You have seen my baby being formed in my body. Even though I can't see her and sometimes thoughts of fear and doubt surround me, I choose to trust in You. You will watch over my baby all the days of her life.

How Your Baby is Growing

Your sweet baby is now the size of a kiwi. All of his major body systems are in place.

He can soon open and close his fingers. He is also looking more like a baby now. Nerves are continuing to form and the nervous system is developing.

Even the thyroid is starting to secrete hormones. Baby now looks like a little human.

How Your Life is Changing

As the first trimester starts to come to an end, you will most likely be feeling much better. You should be able to hear your baby's heartbeat at your doctor's appointment on the doppler. It will be a wonderful sound and you may feel like laughing or crying tears of joy.

You are probably beginning to sport a small baby bump, too. It may be time to do some shopping!

What the Word Says

Shouts of joy and victory resound in the tents of the righteous: "The LORD's right hand has done mighty things!"

Psalm 118:15 NIV

But God had special plans for me and set me apart for his work even before I was born. He called me through His grace.

Galatians 1:15 NCV

This Week's Confession of Faith

Thank you, Father, that my sweet little "kiwi" is functioning like a little human inside my womb. I thank You that You have such special plans for my little baby. By Your grace, You have called him and set him apart. He will glorify You all the days of his life.

I thank You for helping me through this first trimester and that You have never left my side. I praise You and give You glory for You have done great things! You are worthy of all my praise. You are the one that has created this miracle inside of me. I am in awe of Your goodness to me. I love You, Lord!

How Your Baby is Growing

This week, sweet baby is about three inches long and the size of an egg.

She has fingerprints now and you can see her veins and organs through her super thin skin.

If you are having a girl, she already has eggs in her ovaries.

How Your Life is Changing

You may finally be starting to feel better. The morning sickness should be fading and you may actually feel hungry!

You may be starting to "show" and finally looking pregnant.

Your breasts are already making colostrum (the rich fluid filled with nutrients that will feed the baby the first few days after birth before the milk comes in) and you may notice it leaking from time to time.

What the Word Says

Can a woman forget the baby she nurses? Can she feel no kindness for the child to which she gave birth? Even if she could forget her children, I will not forget you. See, I have written your name on my hand.

Isaiah 49:15-16 NCV

My Father gave my sheep to me. He is greater than all, and no person steal my sheep out of my Father's hand.

John 10:29 NCV

This Week's Confession of Faith

Father, I praise You for my sweet baby and that she has fingerprints now. You designed her to be special long ago and will never forget her because You have her engraved on Your hand. I thank You for this and that You love her so much.

I also praise You that You love me so much, too. You have me engraved on Your hand as well and nobody can change that. I thank You that I can rest in You during this pregnancy because You care about it more than I do. Praise You, Father!

How Your Baby is Growing

Baby is about the size of a lemon this week. Only weighing about 1.5 ounces, his body is now covered in soft baby hair.

He can release urine now and suck his little thumb. His liver is making bile and he may be able to hiccup, too.

How Your Life is Changing

Now that you are in the second trimester, your energy level is probably rising. Hopefully, morning sickness is behind you or quickly diminishing.

As your stomach grows, you may be more likely to have some heartburn and indigestion (check out our section for How to Deal with Heartburn).

Sleeping may be becoming harder as your stomach starts to grow. Also, you may need to start shopping for some maternity clothes (check out page 159 for our favorite places to go).

What the Word Says

Acheerful disposition is good for your health; gloom and doom leave you bone-tired.

Proverbs 17:22 MSG

Every day is hard for those who suffer, but a happy heart is like a continual feast.

Proverbs 15:15 NCV

This Week's Confession of Faith

Father, my heart is happy because You have given me this beautiful gift of a child. Although he only weighs a little over an ounce and is still growing, You see his potential and his future. I will choose to be happy today because You have blessed me with this baby and I will carry him with a happy heart.

I choose today to see the good in this pregnancy. Even though I may have some heartburn or difficulty in sleeping, this gift of a child far outweighs any of the physical symptoms I may experience. I choose to feed on this feast of happiness all throughout this pregnancy.

How Your Baby is Growing

This week, sweet baby is about the size of a small orange. She can stretch and bend her arms and legs. Her taste buds are also forming.

She can sense light even though her eyes are still fused shut. If you were to shine a light at your tummy, she would probably move away from it.

How Your Life is Changing

Sometimes the increased blood flow and hormonal changes can cause a stuffy nose. This is very common and is called "rhinitis of pregnancy". Some women even experience nosebleeds.

Round ligament pain is also common during the second trimester. It is pain more commonly felt on the right side of the uterus and is just caused by ligaments stretching.

If the pain becomes severe, call your doctor right away. Otherwise, a heating pad and changing positions carefully will help.

What the Word Says

Taste and see that the LORD is good. Oh, the joys of those who take refuge in him!

Psalm 34:8

How sweet are your words to my taste, sweeter than honey to my mouth!

Psalm 119:103 NIV

This Week's Confession of Faith

Father, thank You that as my baby's taste buds begin to develop that she will always know that the best thing to taste is You! Your Word is sweet and will satisfy her all the days of her life. Nothing is sweeter than being in Your presence and experiencing Your great joy.

Father, as I progress in my pregnancy, I praise You that I am filled with joy because I rest in You. I trust in Your words and Your promises every single day of this pregnancy.

How Your Baby is Growing

Sweet baby is getting ready for a growth spurt! Although only the size of an avocado now, during the next few weeks, he will double his weight and grow longer.

He's starting to grow toenails now and his heart is continuing to increase the amount of blood it is pumping. He may even have hair begging to grow on his scalp.

How Your Life is Changing

You are probably feeling pretty good and anticipating one of the greatest moments of pregnancy – when you feel your baby move.

Some women may notice little flutters around 16 weeks, but don't get discouraged if you aren't feeling him right now. Sometimes it is closer to 20 weeks before any movement is felt.

What the Word Says

Your unfailing love is better than life itself; how I praise you!

Psalm 63:3

The LORD will keep you from all harm- he will watch over your life.

Psalm 121:7 NIV

This Week's Confession of Faith

Thank You, Lord, that You are the Author of life. You have given my baby life and as I anticipate feeling him move this week, I am so thankful. You love me so much and have given me the greatest gift. I am nothing without Your love!

Father, I love Your Word! It's incredibly rich to me. You have promised me that You will keep me from all harm and watch over my life. I trust You to do that now- not only during my pregnancy, but in all the days to follow. Thank You, Jesus!

How Your Baby is Growing

Your baby is about the size of a red onion this week. He can sense sounds and move his joints around.

You are more than likely feeling movement by this time and he can hear your voice, although he may not be able to distinguish it yet.

Talk to him a lot! Pray and sing! He will hear it.

How Your Life is Changing

You have probably gained some weight now and are starting to have a good sized baby bump. You should feel very special to be growing a life.

Remember to eat sensibly and drink lots of water to stay hydrated. This will allow you to feel even better and raise your energy level.

What the Word Says

The eyes of the LORD watch over those who do right; his ears are open to their cries for help.

Psalm 34:15

You will eat the fruit of your labor; blessings and prosperity will be yours.

Psalm 128:2 NIV

This Week's Confession of Faith

Thank You, Father, that as my baby's ears have begun to function, that he hears Your voice. I request that my baby's hearing be perfect physically and that he also be sensitive to hearing Your will for his life.

Praise You for the promise that the fruit of my labor – this child – will be a blessing to me and will prosper me in so many ways for the rest of my life.

How Your Baby is Growing

Baby is the size of a grapefruit this week. The uterus and fallopian tubes are in place if you are having a girl and the genitals are noticeable if you are having a boy.

Her nerves are being covered with protective myelin and will continue to be even after she is born.

How Your Life is Changing

You may notice a few stretch marks and itchy skin beginning to form from your stretching tummy. Hopefully, nausea is a thing of the past and food probably tastes really good to you right now!

Enjoy each moment. Your pregnancy is a precious gift.

What the Word Says

And people should eat and drink and enjoy the fruits of their labor, for these are gifts from God.

Ecclesiastes 3:13

They will come home and sing songs of joy on the heights of Jerusalem. They will be radiant because of the LORD's good gifts.

Jeremiah 31:12

This Week's Confession of Faith

Father, I give thanks to You for my little baby. Even though I may not know if it is a boy or girl yet, You already know. I thank You that his or her reproductive organs form and function perfectly the way that You created them to. In Jesus' name.

I feel happy and hungry, not only for physical food, but also for spiritual food. Your Word has given me so many promises for this time in my life and I am radiant because of Your good gifts!

How Your Baby is Growing

Sweet baby is the size of a large tomato this week. His internal organs are continuing to grow and function.

His arms and legs are in the correct proportion to each other. He is now covered in vernix, which is a white, cheesy substance that is like cream and will protect his skin from the long time he is resting in the amniotic fluid.

How Your Life is Changing

Your tummy is probably pretty round at this point and growing!

Your back may be feeling the effects, so rest often and use a heating pad occasionally to soothe the achy, tired muscles.

What the Word Says

My people will live in safety, quietly at home. They will be at rest.

Isaiah 32:18

God is all strength for his people, Lord, ample refuge for his chosen.

Psalm 28:8 MSG

This Week's Confession of Faith

Father – You are so wonderful and good! You have created a protective covering for my baby's skin while he is submerged in fluid. I pray now that You continue to protect him all the days of his life. Thank You that he has a calm spirit and is at rest.

I give praise to You that You have equipped me with strength! As my body changes and grows, Your strength is what gets me through each day. Thank You, Jesus!

How Your Baby is Growing

Congratulations! You are halfway there. Baby is now the size of a banana. She is working on filling out and getting bigger.

Her teeth are starting to appear and she is swallowing more now. She has also started producing a black sticky substance called meconium which is a by-product of digestion.

How Your Life is Changing

This week is a great milestone. Your uterus is now level with your belly button. Not only are you halfway through your pregnancy, but you should be getting the "big ultrasound" sometime soon. This tends to be a very exciting time with lots of emotions. You might laugh when you see your baby on the screen, you might cry tears of joy when you find out the sex, and you might be overwhelmed all at the same time.

What the Word Says

Being strengthened with all power according to his glorious might so that you may have great endurance and patience.

Colossians 1:11 NIV

And patience produces character, and character produces hope.

Romans 5:4 NCV

This Week's Confession of Faith

Lord, I am excited to see my baby this week on ultrasound. May I never lose sight of where these happy moments came from.

They are all from You and without You, none of this would be possible. You are awesome!

Ultrasound at 20 Weeks

Usually, 20 weeks marks the "big ultrasound" that everyone waits for. My sister is a registered sonographer. That's a fancy name for an ultrasound tech. She does lots of ultrasounds and so I asked her some questions that we would all love to know the answer to!

1. *What do you see during this ultrasound?*
    At your 20 week ultrasound you can expect to find out your baby's progress in reference to weight/age and if baby's organs are all there, and the gender.

2. *How long does it take?* It takes approx 45 minutes to 1.5 hours, depending on how baby is laying and if he/she is being cooperative.

3. *What are you looking for?* We do several different measurements at the 20 week ultrasound. BPD (biparietal diameter) is the measurement of the fetus' head from one ear to the other ear. The HC is the head circumference. The AC is the abdominal circumference and the FL is the length of the femur or thigh bone. These four measurements are used to determine the weight of the fetus. There are also other measurements that will be taken to ensure the overall health of fetus. For instance, we check the LVW (lateral ventricle) to check for hydrocephalus, the Cisterna Magnum which is a space behind the hind brain (cerebellum) that holds spinal fluid, and then the AFI which is the amniotic fluid. We look for the presence of the stomach, four chamber heart, bladder, two kidneys, the cord inser-

tion, how many vessels the umbilical cord is made up of, and many other important organs.

20 Week Ultrasound

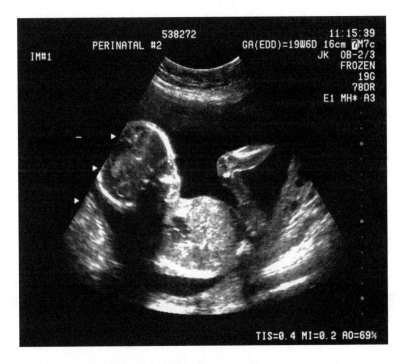

4.   The most annoying question you get asked as a sonographer is, "Can you tell what the gender is?" Be careful not to ask this a lot. Most of the time we will be able to tell the gender, but our number one priority is the health of the fetus.

5.   I think one of the happiest moments of being a sonographer is at the early ultrasound, seeing the heartbeat for the first time...LIFE!

How Your Baby is Growing

Little baby is about the length of a carrot this week. Her eyelids and eyebrows are now visible and you should be able to feel her pretty well now, doing her acrobatic moves. She is putting on fat layers and filling out. You might start to feel her hiccup too!

How Your Life is Changing

You are probably feeling good at this point. You got to see your baby on ultrasound and the reality of having her here with you is so close.

You might start to see a pattern of when she wiggles at certain times of the day.

Don't feel funny about talking or singing to her. It helps you to bond with her.

What the Word Says

The LORD's name should be praised from where the sun rises to where it sets.

Psalm 113:3 NCV

By his power we live and move and exist.

Acts 17:28 NCV

This Week's Confession of Faith

I thank You, Father, that my baby is growing more each day. I ask that as she makes more progress, that I remember that it is by Your power that she lives and moves and exists. Great and mighty are You, Lord!

I will praise You all day long! As I bond with my baby, may I keep my focus on You and praise Your name from the time the sun rises until it sets.

How Your Baby is Growing

This week, your baby is the length of a spaghetti squash and weighs almost one pound. He is beginning to look like a mini-newborn.

His senses are developing and he can hear your heart and your breathing. He can wiggle his fingers and suck his thumb.

His lungs are going through the breathing motions.

How Your Life is Changing

You might be craving some pretty crazy food combinations at this point. Go ahead and indulge as long as you don't overdo it.

Your fingernails and hair may be growing quickly and seem thicker than normal. You may even have a glow to your skin. Smile, because you are beautiful and you are taking part in one of the most precious experiences of your life.

What the Word Says

Let everything that breathes sing praises to the LORD. Praise the LORD!

Psalm 150:6

You are altogether beautiful, my darling, beautiful in every way.

Song of Solomon 4:7

This Week's Confession of Faith

Father, I thank You that as my baby begins to go through the breathing motions in his development, You perfect his lungs and his breath. More importantly, I pray that he always has Your praise on his breath.

I thank You, Lord, that You see me as a beautiful creation. May I see myself the same way, as my womb is a home for a beautiful gift. May I shine for others to be drawn to Your beauty that is within me.

How Your Baby is Growing

Your baby is the size of a cantaloupe this week. You may be able to see her moving around some in your tummy.

Her ears are becoming increasingly keen and are starting to pick up sounds in the outside world. In fact, if she hears a rather loud noise, she may decide to kick or squirm a little.

How Your Life is Changing

You may find that your ankles swell a little at the end of the day. This is completely normal (unless they swell very large, very quickly).

Your circulation in your legs is a little bit sluggish and you might also have some water retention.

If you drink lots of water and avoid sitting for too long, then it should help with swelling.

What the Word Says

So then faith comes by hearing, and hearing by the word of God.

Romans 10:17 NKJV

Lord, hear my voice. Let your ears be attentive to my cry for mercy.

Psalm 130:2 NIV

This Week's Confession of Faith

Father, thank You that my faith comes by hearing Your Word. I use my faith right now to declare that my baby's hearing will develop properly and that she will always be sensitive to hear Your voice.

As I progress in my pregnancy, I praise You Father that You always hear my prayer and my cries for help. Thank You that You are always listening to me. I give You praise for that! In Jesus' name, amen.

How Your Baby is Growing

Baby is really growing well this week. Having put on almost half a pound since last week, he is still pretty lean. He is about as long as an ear of corn.

His lungs and brain are continuing to develop rapidly.

His ears, eyebrows and lashes, fingernails and toenails, are all done!

How Your Life is Changing

Your uterus is now the size of a soccer ball and is above your belly button.

Sometime between this week and week 28, you will have a glucose screening test that tests for gestational diabetes, which is a pregnancy-related high-blood-sugar condition.

You can read more about it at **http://www.ba-bycenter.com/0_glucose-screening-and-glucose-tolerance-tests_1483.bc**

What the Word Says

The righteous cry out, and the LORD hears them; he delivers them from all their troubles.

Psalm 34:17 NIV

God's Word is better than a diamond, better than a diamond set between emeralds. You'll like it better than strawberries in spring, better than red, ripe strawberries.

Psalm 19:10 MSG

This Week's Confession of Faith

Father, thank You that my baby's lungs will be strong! He will have a strong cry at birth and beyond. I give praise to You for hearing our cries and bringing deliverance to us always. Hallelujah!

As I go for my sugar test soon, Lord, I thank You that Your Word is sweeter than any food that I consume. It meets all of my needs and calms all of my fears. Your Word is so precious and rich. Thank You, Lord.

How Your Baby is Growing

Baby is about the size of a loaf of bread. He's getting fattened up and starting to look more and more like a newborn.

His hair should be visible now and you can see the texture and color.

His lungs are developing rapidly, along with his respiratory system.

How Your Life is Changing

You might be noticing that you are not as graceful as you once were. Moving around might start to be a little difficult.

Your body is probably craving some good sleep, too. You might try a body pillow to get comfortable. Remember that you are supposed to lie on your side to allow for the blood to circulate easily.

What the Word Says

Jesus answered by quoting Deuteronomy: "It takes more than bread to stay alive. It takes a steady stream of words from God's mouth."

Matthew 4:4 MSG

May God our Father and the Lord Jesus Christ give you grace and peace.

Philippians 1:2

This Week's Confession of Faith

Father, as my baby is gaining weight and getting to be bigger, may he always realize that it is You that will satisfy his hunger. He will need to eat food, but the best food is Your Word. May he always hunger for the things of You.

Lord, I may not be too graceful right now but You are always giving me grace and for that I am thankful! You give me so much more than I deserve. You bless me because You are so good. There's nothing that I can do to deserve Your blessings. Thank You, Lord!

How Your Baby is Growing

Baby is about 14 inches from head to toe now and weighs over a pound and a half. She can open her eyes, which were previously fused shut, and she is also practicing her breathing.

She can move small amounts of amniotic fluid through her lungs now as they are continuing to develop.

How Your Life is Changing

You might have experienced some leg cramps, especially during the night. Stretching carefully and slowly, as well as incorporating more magnesium into your diet (bananas and beans) will help.

You may also have experienced some constipation. Drinking more water and getting more fiber in your diet should help resolve that uncomfortable issue.

What the Word Says

My eyes are always looking to the LORD for help. He will keep me from any traps.

Psalm 25:15 NCV

He satisfies the thirsty and fills up the hungry.

Psalm 107:9 NCV

This Week's Confession of Faith

Thank You, Lord, that my baby is going to have great eyesight! I pray also that her eyes are always on You. May she follow You in everything that she does and look to You always.

I praise You, Father, for giving me everything that I need. In this natural body, I may get thirsty for water but in my spirit, I will get thirsty for You and Your Word. Thank You that You always fill me up. I love You, Lord!

How Your Baby is Growing

Baby is around two pounds this week and about the size of an eggplant. He is probably sucking his fingers and has regular intervals of sleeping and waking.

His lungs can breathe air and his brain stem can regulate rhythmic breathing, as well as his body temperature.

How Your Life is Changing

As the second trimester draws to a close, you are probably feeling your baby move regularly. He should move 10 times an hour during his active periods.

You should call your doctor if you don't feel him moving for several hours in a row.

What the Word Says

Let everything that breathes praise the Lord. Praise the Lord!

Psalm 150:6 NCV

For in him we live and move and exist.

Acts 17:28

This Week's Confession of Faith

Thank You, Father, that my baby breathes deeply and that his lungs are strong! As he breathes air here on earth, may he also breathe the wonderful things of Your Spirit. May he always be full of praise to You!

Lord, I live and move and exist in You and because of You. As I feel my baby move in my womb, may I always be reminded that it is You who gives life. Thank you Lord, for this precious gift!

How Your Baby is Growing

Baby now weighs over two pounds and is around 15 inches long. She can sense light and can blink her eyes.

She can turn her head from side to side and may have a full head of hair.

How Your Life is Changing

Welcome to the third trimester! You may be experiencing some Braxton Hicks contractions by now, which are "practice" contractions. It will feel like your tummy is tightening and then relaxing.

Usually, a warm bath will help lessen the contractions as it helps the body relax or try drinking a couple of glasses of water. Sometimes, Braxton Hicks contractions are brought on by dehydration. If they don't let up and are painful, then be sure to call your doctor.

What the Word Says

You are the giver of life. Your light lets us enjoy life.

Psalm 36:9 NCV

The night is about over, dawn is about to break. Be up and awake to what God is doing! God is putting the finishing touches on the salvation work he began when we first believed.

Romans 13:12 MSG

This Week's Confession of Faith

Father, only You are the giver of life and the light. I pray that as my baby can sense physical light now, that she will always know the true Light and that is You. I thank You for Your Word that reminds me of how much You love me and that everything You have for me is good.

As I start the third trimester of this pregnancy, I put all of my trust in You. I will be aware of Your Spirit leading me and showing me the truth.

How Your Baby is Growing

Baby is now the size of a butternut squash. He is around 2.5 pounds and his head is getting bigger to make room for his growing brain.

He is hiccupping (which you will be able to feel) and still accumulating fat on his body to fill him out.

How Your Life is Changing

You are making a turn towards the home stretch. You might be experiencing frequent trips to the restroom as your baby presses on your bladder.

You also may have experienced those awful hemorrhoids due to your growing uterus. They are common and usually a sitz bath or cold medicated compresses can help relieve the pain.

What the Word Says

For I have always been mindful of your unfailing love and have lived in reliance on your faithfulness.

Psalm 26:3 NIV

Don't be afraid, for I am with you. Don't be discouraged, for I am your God. I will strengthen you and help you. I will hold you up with my victorious right hand.

Isaiah 41:10

This Week's Confession of Faith

Father, You are always faithful. I thank You that You love my baby more than I ever could. I speak over my baby that as his body systems continue to develop, that they be strong and whole in Jesus' name.

Father, I refuse to fear about the upcoming days. Even if I have bad days where I don't feel just right, I will put my whole trust in You. I refuse to be discouraged about anything because You have promised to strengthen and help me. Thank you, Jesus!

How Your Baby is Growing

Baby weighs around three pounds this week and is about the size of a head of cabbage. His eyesight is continuing to develop and his sweet face looks much like it will when you see him for the first time.

He still needs to gain some weight but he can now open his eyes, move his head, and his nostrils are open.

How Your Life is Changing

You have some choices coming up like whether to breastfeed or formula feed; what to name your baby; where to give birth-- a hospital or a birthing center; whether to take the epidural or go the natural route.

Just remember to follow peace through it all. Stress isn't good for making proper decisions, or for your physical body.

What the Word Says

The LORD bless you and keep you; the LORD make his face shine on you and be gracious to you. The LORD turn his face toward you and give you peace.

Numbers 6:24-26 NIV

The LORD gives his people strength. The LORD blesses them with peace.

Psalm 29:11

This Week's Confession of Faith

Lord, as I prepare to see my sweet baby's face, I thank You that Your face is shining on both of us. His face is a reflection of Your love for me. I thank You for shining Your light on my baby's face, both in the womb and out.

I praise You, Father, that You lead me in peace. Your ways and Your thoughts should give me peace. Father, help me to be sensitive to follow in Your peace and not anyone else's opinions. Thank You for Your sweet peace that encompasses me now.

How Your Baby is Growing

At just over three pounds, your baby will put on a half a pound a week from now until right at the end of your pregnancy. She's probably pretty active now and sometimes may keep you up at night. This just means she is doing what she is supposed to do!

Her head could be full of hair but her skull is still soft because the bones have not fused together yet. This is necessary for her to pass through the birth canal. She will keep a soft spot on her head for about a year after she is born.

How Your Life is Changing

You will probably continue to experience some Braxton Hicks contractions. We covered those a few weeks ago. Remember to stay hydrated. Water is so good for you right now.

Your baby might kick your bladder and you might feel a sudden urge to go to the bathroom. The pressure of the baby and the extra weight may be taking a toll on your lower back and hips. A prenatal massage can help with those aches and pains.

What the Word Says

A thief comes to steal and kill and destroy, but I came to give life – life in all its fullness.

John 10:10 NCV

If anyone believes in me, rivers of living water will flow out from that person's heart.

John 7:38 NCV

This Week's Confession of Faith

Thank You, Father, that my baby is full of life! You came to give us life and I speak Your life to her in Jesus' name. As she moves in my womb, may I always be reminded that You want her to experience the fullness that You sent Jesus to give her. Thank You for Your sacrifice!

Lord, as I drink earthly water to keep myself hydrated, I thank You that because I know You, rivers of living water flow out of my heart.

How Your Baby is Growing

Your baby is packing on the weight from now until the end. The latest research has shown that by this point, babies have developed sensitivity to temperature. If you were to put an ice pack on your belly, he might give you a kick or two.

Most babies, at this point, are in a head down position. He is also probably in a routine where he sleeps at certain times and is active at others. After he is born, he will most likely keep the same routine.

How Your Life is Changing

Your lower back may begin to hurt due to your growing uterus and the hormonal changes that loosen the ligaments and joints. It can be really hard to sit for a long period of time, get off the floor, or roll over in bed.

If your back is hurting excessively or pain seems to come out of nowhere, notify your doctor, as this could be a sign of pre-term labor.

You may also notice some fluid leaking from your breasts. This is called colostrum and will be what your baby feeds on for the first couple of days of his life.

What the Word Says

How great is the goodness you have stored up for those who fear you. You lavish it on those who come to you for protection, blessing them before the watching world.

Psalm 31:19

Everyone will share the story of your wonderful goodness; they will sing with joy about your righteousness.

Psalm 145:7

This Week's Confession of Faith

Father, thank You that You have so many good things stored up for me and my baby. You love to give us good things because we come to You and we live for You. I am overwhelmed by Your love for this baby. You love him more than I do. I thank You that Your plans are only good for him.

Lord, even though I may be feeling uncomfortable, I still want to have a grateful heart. Because of Your goodness, I am blessed with the gift of a child. May my heart always sing of Your love.

How Your Baby is Growing

Baby is now a little over four pounds. She is looking like a small little newborn. She is getting stronger and her movements can be painful to you sometimes.

As she grows, the amount of movement will decrease some because she is running out of room. However, if you haven't felt her move in an hour or so, drink something cold and lay down (preferably on your side). If she still doesn't want to move for you, calling the doctor is a good precaution.

How Your Life is Changing

You may feel a little short of breath and that can be completely normal. As baby gets bigger, your uterus and internal organs are being crowded and pushed around.

You may also seem to be waddling instead of walking. Watch out for your big bump because it can definitely seem to want to run into things! Be in tune with your baby and make sure she is moving around throughout the day.

What the Word Says

You have made known to me the path of life; you will fill me with joy in your presence, with eternal pleasures at your right hand.

Psalm 16:11 NIV

The LORD will keep you from all harm – he will watch over your life.

Psalm 121:7 NIV

This Week's Confession of Faith

Thank You, Father, that You are watching over my baby. As she moves around, I continue to speak life and health over her. You are keeping her from all harm and watching over her life. I am thankful that I can rest in Your promise and not worry about what is going on in my womb. You have Your hand on my sweet child.

Lord, I thank You for filling me with Your joy. My hormones and body may be going wacky, but You remain constant in my life and for that, I am grateful.

How Your Baby is Growing

Baby now weighs well over four pounds and is about the size of a cantaloupe. His lungs continue to mature, as does his central nervous system. His liver is still working on maturing, too, thus the reason that a lot of newborns get jaundice. Sometimes, during this week, your baby will "drop," meaning that his head is situated in your pelvis in birth-ready position. If your baby is breech, your doctor might discuss options with you about turning the baby or a having a C-section.

How Your Life is Changing

As baby drops into your pelvis, you may feel lots of back pain and even sciatic nerve pain as the weight is shifted to the pelvic region. Warm baths and a heating pad when needed can really help.

Also, stretch and change positions to see if you can get baby off of the sciatic nerve. Lots of rest during these next few weeks is important. If you can even manage a catnap here and there, it will help.

What the Word Says

Even strong young lions sometimes go hungry, but those who trust in the LORD will lack no good thing.

Psalm 34:10

But all who listen to me will live in peace, untroubled by fear of harm.

Proverbs 1:33

This Week's Confession of Faith

Father, thank You for Your promise that everyone who trusts in You will lack no good thing. You provide for me everything that I need. When my mind starts to worry or fear about providing for this child, may I always remember Your promise to me.

Thank You, Lord, that I can have peace. I don't have to be fearful of other's experiences, but I can trust totally in You. That is what You want from us, and so I commit to trust You right now. I will not be afraid.

How Your Baby is Growing

Your sweet baby now weighs in at over five pounds. Her kidneys are all done developing and her liver is starting to process some waste.

She is continuing to put on fat layers and the soft hair that covered her body early on is now disappearing. She has also probably developed a sleeping pattern, which you should be able to notice by her quiet times and her active times. This can hold true to life outside the womb, so be prepared.

How Your Life is Changing

You are probably feeling pretty cramped in every way – your clothes, your bed, your internal organs. Your uterus now reaches up to your rib cage. You will start seeing your doctor every week now.

It won't be much longer until you will be holding your sweet baby. You probably want to start thinking about your options for labor and delivery – natural, epidural, if you want a birth plan of any kind. You should start writing your plans down so that you don't have to worry about that once the time comes.

What the Word Says

We are pressed on every side by troubles, but we are not crushed. We are perplexed, but not driven to despair. We are hunted down, but never abandoned by God. We get knocked down, but we are not destroyed.

2 Corinthians 4:8-9

We do not want you to become lazy, but to imitate those who through faith and patience inherit what has been promised.

Hebrews 6:12 NIV

This Week's Confession of Faith

Father, thank You that even though I may be feeling pressed on every side, You will never abandon me and I will never be driven to despair. You will get me through this and anything else I might face.

Thank You, Father, for this sweet baby that I have waited patiently for. Help me not to lose my faith and patience during this last month, but to draw from Your strength in everything that I do. I will inherit what has been promised to me if I do not give up.

How Your Baby is Growing

Your little one weighs in at six pounds this week and his length hovers around 13.2 inches (crown to rump). Your once wiggly baby now favors certain body positions.

Typically, your baby will enjoy resting with his head down and his rump toward your ribs—the ideal placement for delivery. Your baby's movements will become less frequent as he has less wiggle room.

From now, baby's growth will be slow and steady as he continues to put on weight and fill out.

How Your Life is Changing

You've now entered the final month of pregnancy—congratulations! You're probably anxious to meet your new baby and be rid of the discomforts of pregnancy. Heartburn may be a constant complaint. As your stomach is pushed upward by your ever-expanding uterus, acid from the stomach may leak back into your esophagus (acid reflux). Slow digestion caused by pregnancy also worsens the affects of heartburn since food sits in your stomach longer. You may be feeling really tired and low on energy. You may also have some swelling in your ankles after a long day, especially if the weather is warm.

What the Word Says

I can do all things through Christ, because he gives me strength.

Philippians 4:13 NCV

And God's peace, which is so great we cannot understand it, will keep your hearts and minds in Christ Jesus.

Philippians 4:7 NCV

This Week's Confession of Faith

Thank You, Lord, for giving me strength. You have been with me all the way and You are still with me. I will not give up. I will not give in. I will rely on Your strength, which allows me to face anything.

Father, Your Word says that You will bless me with peace that nobody can understand completely. It will take over and control how I feel and what I think. Nothing is better than Your peace and I thank You right now for it in Jesus' name. Amen.

How Your Baby is Growing

Congratulations! You are now full term. Your baby is done developing and is ready to come out during the next few weeks.

Baby is weighing about six pounds right now. Most boys weigh more than girls at this point. Baby might have a full head of hair or she might be totally bald.

She is getting very ready to meet you!

How Your Life is Changing

You are probably watching for the early signs of labor which can include:

- More frequent and stronger Braxton Hicks contractions.
- Loss of your mucus plug. This is the "plug" of mucus that has kept your cervical canal blocked all these months. It can be tinged with blood, known as "bloody show", and may come out all at once or a little at a time.
- Increased vaginal discharge.

What the Word Says

Do not worry about anything, but pray and ask God for everything you need, always giving thanks.

Philippians 4:6 NCV

All praise to God, the Father of our Lord Jesus Christ, who has blessed us with every spiritual blessing in the heavenly realms because we are united with Christ.

Ephesians 1:3

This Week's Confession of Faith

Father, Your Word tells me not to worry but to pray and ask You for everything I need. I ask You now for a healthy baby and a healthy momma at the end of this journey. I give this care over to You and I will trust You with this request.

Lord, You have blessed me. Because I am united with Christ, I have every spiritual blessing available in the heavenly realms. I can enjoy life, peace, health, and grace to get through each day. Thank You, Jesus.

How Your Baby is Growing

Weighing well over six pounds, your baby is ready to face the world! All of his organs are mature and he is ready to grab your fingers as you hold hands for the first time.

He is likely pretty cramped in your uterus now and not doing a whole lot of moving. You should still monitor his movements and kicks though, to make sure he is staying active.

If you are worried or feel that he is not moving like he should, then call your healthcare provider just to

How Your Life is Changing

Some things to watch out for here at the end are:
- sudden or extreme swelling of feet, hands, or face
- severe headaches
- double or blurred vision
- upper abdominal pain or nausea and vomiting

All of these symptoms can be a sign of preeclampsia. It causes the blood vessels to constrict resulting in high blood pressure. Less blood flow to the uterus can mean problems for your baby as well so be sure to report any of these symptoms right away.

What the Word Says

You, LORD, give true peace to those who depend on you, because they trust you.

Isaiah 26:3 NCV

All your children will be taught by the LORD, and they will have much peace.

Isaiah 54:13 NCV

This Week's Confession of Faith

Father, You are the Author of peace. You have promised to give me peace when I depend on You. Peace allows my body and my mind to relax and not be uptight. I receive this promise from You now.

Thank You, Lord, that this child will also have much peace because he is taught by You. I speak peace to him, that all the days of his life he will know in his heart that You are the answer for everything he needs.

How Your Baby is Growing

Baby is continuing to put on fat layers, but she is done developing! She probably weighs a little over seven pounds and is around 20 inches long (this is the average). You are so ready to hear her cry for the first time, signaling that she is in the world and communicating with you.

Continue to talk to her and read to her. She may turn her face toward you when she first arrives. If you haven't already packed your hospital bag, now would be a good time. We have a good list of items to include in that bag on pg. 160.

How Your Life is Changing

You are probably a ball of emotions. One minute you might feel so ready to see your baby and the next, you might be sad that the pregnancy is coming to an end. You are almost there. You have done such a great job carrying your baby to the end! Don't get discouraged. She will come out in due time! What a precious time awaits you and your family.

Whether this is your first child or your fifth, the excitement and anticipation remains the same. This might also be a good time to get one last dinner date in with your hubby and spend some quality time together.

What the Word Says

Therefore, since we are surrounded by such a huge crowd of witnesses to the life of faith, let us strip off every weight that slows us down, especially the sin that so easily trips us up. And let us run with endurance the race God has set before us.

Hebrews 12:1

I have fought the good fight, I have finished the race, and I have remained faithful.

2 Timothy 4:7

This Week's Confession of Faith

Thank You, Father, that I am almost ready to meet my child. This has been a journey and You have never left my side. Thank You for giving me the endurance that I need to finish this course with excellence. I will not give up, but will look to You for my strength.

Lord, You have been so faithful to me through all of this. Your Word never changes and I am so thankful that I can rely on Your Word and Your promises. Now, as I head to the last part of my journey in labor and delivery, I thank You that I can finish well. Hallelujah!

Congratulations!
You Reached Week 40

You have reached the end of your journey. While your doctor may allow you to go a little past 40 weeks, most babies are born before or during this week.

If you are still struggling with fears of the labor and delivery, keep resting in the promises throughout this book. The Word of God is the best book you can read to prepare you for your labor and delivery and your journey into parenthood.

Trust Him – He won't let you down!

Final Scriptures

For the word of the LORD holds true, and we can trust everything he does.

Psalm 33:4

It is better to take refuge in the LORD than to trust in people.

Psalm 118:8

For if we are faithful to the end, trusting God just as firmly as when we first believed, we will share in all that belongs to Christ.

Hebrews 3:14

Now all glory to God, who is able, through his mighty power at work within us, to accomplish infinitely more than we might ask or think.

Ephesians 3:20

May the LORD bless you
and protect you.
May the LORD smile on you
and be gracious to you.
May the LORD show you his favor
and give you his peace.
Numbers 6:24-26

Tips for the Mom to Be

How We Got Through Morning Sickness

Julie – I couldn't stand to eat anything really sweet in the mornings because it would make me really nauseous, so I needed some protein. However, the smell of bacon and eggs wasn't very appealing, either. So, after racking my brain on what would taste good – I came up with a protein shake. I had some special protein powder mix (check with your doctor on which brand to use) and added some peanut butter and milk in the blender with ice to make it really cold. It was such a welcome breakfast and loaded me full of protein so my blood sugar stabilized. Try it, you might love it!

Tonya – Whenever the girls at the office would want to go out to eat during lunch, I would just cringe. I was nauseous all day long and the only thing that I could eat was a plain Arby's roast beef sandwich. The protein and iron helped me not feel as tired, too.

Ann – I wanted to drink something carbonated but knew that soda was bad for me. I found these really cool, plastic bottles of Perrier water at the grocery store. The water is carbonated and especially good after being in the fridge for a few hours. This helped me stay away from soda, but also provided that carbonation that settled my stomach.

Danielle – Someone told me that peppermint calmed the stomach, so I was constantly chewing on peppermints and candy canes. It really did help!

Andrea – I got through morning sickness with lots of comfort food like grilled cheese sandwiches and macaroni and cheese.

How We Dealt with Those Swollen Ankles

Sara – I made my husband give me a foot massage every night!

Julie – I slept in my recliner!

Leah – I would put ice packs on my feet. (It was August!)

Tami – I wore slippers around everywhere!

Andrea – I would lie on a float in the pool and relax.

Best Way to Get to Sleep

Leah – I changed positions very frequently! Doctors say to sleep on your left side but it was hard to stay on one side the whole night!

Katie – Sleep on your side with a pillow between your knees.

Joelle – I slept on my side with pillows all around me.

Jenn – Exercising during the day and reading before bed.

Julie – I slept in the recliner a lot.

Ann – Body pillows are the best thing ever invented! You can even have more than one.

Jennifer – A warm bath before bed helped me sleep.

Gayle – Take naps whenever you can.

For Heartburn

Always check with your doctor before taking any medicine, but most will tell you that it is ok to take TUMS. Most of my friends who experienced heartburn during pregnancy took lots of TUMS. Sometimes, it is nice, too, to be aware of what foods might cause heartburn to flare up. Orange juice and salsa were the causes of my heartburn flare-ups. Propping up in bed with a couple of pillows behind you helps, too.

Eating Healthy

It's so hard to eat healthy sometimes, especially when you are nauseous. A few tricks are to juice fruits and veggies and have fruits, veggies and nuts on hand to snack on. Don't deprive yourself of your cravings. That is one of the fun parts about pregnancy. But try to balance it out with the healthy stuff, too.

Best Place to Shop for Maternity Clothes

Target, Motherhood, Old Navy, Craigslist.org and garage sales!

Weirdest Food Craving

Pop, chocolate milkshakes, scrambled eggs, orange juice, pickles, blue Gatorade, uncooked rice (yes – that was me!!)

Food Aversions

Chili, Arby's beef and cheddar sandwiches, chicken, red meat

Best Stress Reliever

Light exercise, a walk around the block, warm bath, heating pad, recliner with feet up, soothing music, massage from my hubby, a bowl of my favorite ice cream, reading the Word and praying

What to Pack in Your Hospital Bag

- Gowns (if you are nursing, then nursing gowns are nice)
- Slippers
- Your own pillow
- Robe
- Nursing pads/bra
- Lanolin cream for your breasts, if nursing
- Snacks
- Baby book to record baby's first moments
- Journal
- Bible
- Maternity outfit to wear home (don't pack your skinny jeans because you probably won't get into them!!)
- Hair dryer
- Your favorite scented shampoo/body wash (you'll want to enjoy that first shower)
- Make-up
- Cell phone charger
- Camera/laptop/iPad/iPod and a charger for each
- Outfit for baby to wear home
- To-call list
- Car seat (this won't fit in your bag, but make sure you bring it to the hospital with you)

Post-Partum Depression

We hear the term "post-partum depression" thrown around all the time, but do women understand what it really is or what to expect when the baby is born? Babycenter.com says that post-partum depression can begin any time during the first two months after you give birth.

Some symptoms include:

- Irritability or hypersensitivity
- Difficulty concentrating
- Anxiety and worry
- Crying or tearfulness
- Anger
- Negative feelings such as sadness, hopelessness, helplessness, or guilt
- Loss of interest in activities you usually enjoy
- Difficulty sleeping (especially returning to sleep)
- Fatigue or exhaustion
- Changes in appetite or eating habits
- Headaches, stomachaches, muscle or backaches

After I had my first son, I wasn't sure what to expect. I thought I knew all about babies from helping take care of my brother, who was born when I was 13, and also from baby-sitting a lot when I was a teenager. However, nothing prepared me for the feelings of inadequacy and exhaustion that I would experience.

Both sets of our parents lived out of state, so when my mom left after being with me for two weeks, I cried for days. It took several months for me to actually want to get out and do something besides just rock the baby in my recliner and cry. I didn't realize at the time that I was suffering from post-partum depression. I never had thoughts of hurting myself or the baby but I sure did want to cry a lot!

During my second pregnancy, I experienced the death of two family members with whom I was very close. Instead of allowing myself to grieve, I held it all in until my second son was born. Then, it was like a floodgate. I cried a lot and felt so sad. I was happy to have a new baby, but I wanted things to be the way they were.

I think we would be lying to ourselves if we said that only a few people experience post-partum depression. I believe that all women go through some different negative feelings with the hormones and the experience of bringing a new life into an already established household. Although you love your baby, you can feel helpless and sad that things aren't the way that they used to be. I think this is normal and I would tell women not to be so hard on themselves. Your whole life has just changed.

Taking all this to heart, if you are having trouble coping, I would make sure you talk to your doctor. Remember all the good promises of God's Word that are included in this book. They can help you get through anything. Having a good friend or family member to talk to is important and if you have a church family, rely on them! That is what they are there for. Take all the help you are offered and remember to offer help to others when they have a new baby. If the weather is nice, make sure and get outside. A lot of times, just being inside a lot will add to the feelings of being down.

Last but not least, focus on the good things. When you start to focus on what is good in your life and not the negative, your outlook begins to change. Although you may have had to have a C-section, be thankful for a healthy baby or if you had a bad birth experience, be thankful you were full term, etc. You can always find something to be thankful for. When you start to focus on being thankful for the good in your life, your whole outlook will change.

> Fix your thoughts on what is true, and honorable, and right, and pure, and lovely, and admirable. Think about things that are excellent and worthy of praise.
> Philippians 4:8

He's the Lifter of My Head

by Destiny

When I first read the results on the positive pregnancy test, I was shocked. So shocked that I peed on it again, hoping it would change the results. It's funny now, but I was in such a state of surprise that it made sense at the time. I was in the middle of a very complicated relationship with my ex-husband. We were separated with plans to file for divorce in a month when we had the money to do so.

It turned into quite an ordeal to find the father of my unborn baby that night. I eventually found him in a bar and steeled myself to tell him. Because he was inebriated, he was thrilled and passed the pregnancy test down the bar. I was scared and embarrassed. The friend who brought him to the bar that night tried to reason with him that I should have an abortion. When he wouldn't budge, she pulled me into the bathroom and tried to pitch the same idea to me. I wouldn't budge but I had thoughts deep down where that option became enticing.

I felt very alone and I was in a new place. We didn't have much money and my husband was in school full time. We slept on a futon mattress on the floor. I was halfway through the pregnancy before we could afford a used mattress for $80. I was also worried about affording maternity clothes and an even greater a worry was how we would afford food.

I had finally started to make a little money at my job when one day at work, my ankles swelled. Not just a little. One of the girls made me sit down and prop up my feet while she got the manager. I wasn't very worried because I had seen them do this before, but everyone else was in awe of how swollen I was. Their reactions started to scare me. When my manager saw my ankles, she told me that I needed to leave right away and go to the doctor and not to come back until the doctor said it was ok.

The doctor's office was already closed that day so I decided to wait until in the morning. My manager called to check on me and was worried that I hadn't made it in to the doctor that day. She told me to go in the morning first thing. I was trying not to panic. I thought it was normal to swell. I had read about pre-eclampsia in my pregnancy book but it said it only happened in about 5% of the pregnancies, so I wasn't too worried about it.

The next morning, preeclampsia is exactly what the doctor diagnosed me with. I was put on moderate bed rest and not allowed to work. This was in the beginning of my third trimester. Finally, as I continued swelling and my blood pressure continued rising, I was admitted to the hospital when I was 33 weeks.

I was in the hospital for a week, battling with my blood pressure. Finally, at 34 weeks, the doctor rushed into my room and said "We need to deliver this baby right now." I had to have a C-section because the doctor didn't think I could handle giving birth without having a seizure.

Kyleigh was born at 6:15 P.M. and weighed 3lbs. 6 oz. She was very healthy, with the exception of her weight. She had to stay in the hospital until she was 4 lbs. 5 oz. and then she got to come home.

I struggled with depression, loneliness, and fear during and after my pregnancy with Kyleigh, but was so thankful after she was born for it to just be over. Through all the adversity that I experienced, God never left my side. Even though things weren't easy and it wasn't something I would choose to go through, I came out stronger. In times of total weakness and pure sadness, the Lord came through. He was truly my protector, my shield, and the lifter of my head.

But you, O LORD, are a shield around me; you are
my glory, the one who holds my head high.
Psalm 3:3

You Were Always with Me

by Julie

When I found out I was pregnant for the second time, I was in a little bit of shock. It wasn't a bad shock at all, but just shock. The pregnancy wasn't planned and I had experienced a complicated pregnancy the first go around. However, I was inwardly excited and the thought of giving my son a sibling made me happy.

The pregnancy started out uneventful. After a few weeks, I began experiencing horrible nausea, just like I did with my first pregnancy. This time, I had a two year old to take care of. My husband was great in the evenings and basically did everything for our son so I could lie on the couch in my comatose state of sleep and nausea.

When I started feeling better around week 14 or so, I was in for another blow. My cousin, Gina, who was more like a sister to me growing up, was fighting cancer. She had been doing well up until this point when she took a sudden and drastic turn for the worse. By the 16th week of my pregnancy, she had been placed on a ventilator. I was still standing for her complete healing and didn't give way to the negative feelings until the last day of her life.

My mom had called and let me know that Gina's blood pressure was dropping and her body was starting to shut down. I couldn't believe it. I cried out to God and asked for a miracle. I couldn't believe we were at this point. On Thursday, April 13th, 2006, at around 8:30 A.M., Gina went to be with Jesus. Just like that – she was gone.

When I received the phone call from my dad, I just went into an emotional blur. I cried and cried, but my husband was already at work and I didn't want to be alone. I went ahead and took my son to preschool and went to work to be around people. Knowing I would be gone for a few days for the funeral, I worked all day in between tears and phone calls. Since it was around tax time, too, my husband and I had to finish up our personal taxes that we had planned to do over the weekend.

By the time we got our taxes done and left the office, it was well after 7 P.M. We ran to get something to eat and back home to pack for a 6 A.M. flight. After needing to go to the bathroom for several hours, I finally went when I got home to find that I was spotting. I was concerned, but figured it had been an extremely stressful day and the blood was brown, so I was hoping it was just old stuff that my body was getting rid of.

Knowing I could get an ultrasound done by my sister when I arrived back home, I went ahead and got on the flight without calling my doctor. I spotted throughout that next day and through the next, until we could get to the hospital for my sister to look at what was going on. She did see my cervix was closed, but I was having contractions. She also let us know that we were having another boy!

I tried to be calm and to breathe deeply, but that's hard when you are so emotional anyway and you are dealing with death, especially the death of someone who shouldn't have died so young. I continued to drink water and keep my emotions at bay.

When I returned home from the funeral, I called my doctor. She got me in right away and also saw that my cervix was closed, but seemed concerned that I was still bleeding.

The week after we returned from Gina's funeral, I got a call on a Thursday night letting me know that my aunt on my dad's side had passed away. It was a complete shock. Although she had faced health problems in the past, she was very active and was doing well. Again, I pushed my emotions away so much so that I couldn't even cry at this point. I knew this wasn't a good thing.

I continued to spot for six weeks until I reached the 23 week mark. As suddenly as the spotting came, it left. However, I was still guarded. I was not going to deal with anything during this pregnancy in case it would affect the baby in a negative way. I felt that I was a little depressed going into the last part of my pregnancy. I wasn't excited about my shower or getting the house ready or anything like that. I just wanted to be left alone and not be around anyone.

As the time for delivery drew closer, I felt like I was in a real slump. I went into labor on my own and everything went smoothly for the most part. We were so glad to welcome Elijah James into our family. He was a beautiful baby and so sweet.

After we got home and were getting adjusted to life as a family of four, all the emotions from the events in the pregnancy welled up. I was sad, angry, happy, and indifferent, all mixed into one. I began to realize that no matter what my circumstances, that the Lord was still there. He never left me or my family. Although we had been through a hard time, His Word didn't change. He didn't change. Circumstances change, but He never does.

I began to lean on Him and rely on His grace to get me through, and you know what? He was faithful, as always. I got through it and I look back now and see Him with me every step of the way.

Jesus Christ is the same yesterday, today and forever.
Hebrews 13:5-8

Getting My Eyes Off Myself

by Lori

My husband and I met in college and got married six months after we graduated. My sweetheart proposed on a gondola in Venice, Italy. My dream had begun, only it did not work out quite as I had planned.

My mother always told me to wait five years after marriage before starting a family, because I would need time to develop my relationship with my husband first. So I waited five years, just as my mother advised. Two years later, we still had not conceived. So at that point we had been married for seven years and had no children. I thought for sure that we would get pregnant right away. In fact, growing up I was always so careful with my virtue because I just knew that the first time I had sex it would surely result in a pregnancy. I was beyond shocked when unprotected sex did not yield a baby for two years!

Month after month, I anxiously checked my fertility calendar, and each and every month, I thought it would be the one. Some months were emotionally harder than others, but after a good cry (when my period finally came) I would move on. I did this for a little over two years, but at some point I got sidetracked from my baby plans.

A friend of our family had been diagnosed with melanoma. He was a 32-year-old handsome, strong, healthy young man up until that point. He loved Jesus and he was dying. My prayer life took a different turn and instead of praying for my needs, I started praying for this young man and his family. My younger brother had a couple of bouts with cancer and so my heart always breaks for others suffering the way my brother did....the way our family did. So I actually forgot about charting ovulation and fussing over when my period was due.

One fine day, after 2 ½ years of trying to conceive, I realized I could be pregnant. I actually noticed my bust size had gotten substantially larger and then it hit me. I ran to the calendar and realized that I was five days late. I was blown away, because I had not even noticed that I was late. I immediately rushed out to the store to buy a pregnancy test.

On the way home from the store I kept thinking of fun ways to tell my husband if I was pregnant. He was at work so I knew that I had a few minutes to make it home and take the test. Two lines showed up immediately and all of my plans to tell him in a clever way went out the window.

As soon as I realized I was pregnant, I lost all my senses. I screamed at the top of my lungs, so he knew what was going on before I even came out of the bathroom! What a surprise! Something wonderful happened in my life when I took my eyes off of myself and prayed for someone else to get their miracle. I don't necessarily think that is the magic recipe for everyone, but God really must have wanted me to take my eyes off of myself for a while.

I once heard a pastor say that if you pray for others to get their breakthrough, then God will see that you get yours. I did not do this intentionally, but it certainly does ring true for me.

Surprisingly enough, when I called to tell my parents, my mom already knew. She actually sent me an email (that I never opened) a few days before I took the pregnancy test asking me if there was any chance I was pregnant. She said that she had a dream that I was holding a baby in my arms and nine months later, that dream (our dream) came true! Praise God!

My pregnancy was perfect, but my delivery was very difficult. I had taken some hippie birthing classes, because that class was the only one I could find and I knew I needed to take something. Somehow I got it in my head that I needed to have a natural, un-medicated childbirth. Well, I had a very difficult natural birth. I was in labor for 24 hours and I pushed for 7 or 8. It was traumatic, to say the least. I will make sure that next time I take the epidural and won't feel condemned about it!

So, because my birth was so difficult, I was really exhausted. My milk supply came in late and was not abundant. I really had difficulties nursing and I wanted my baby to get breast milk so desperately. I had no idea that something that is supposed to be natural can be so very difficult. But I was determined to make it work, so I nursed some and used a breast pump every hour to build my milk supply. I got very little sleep and I became so focused on my milk supply that I kind of lost touch with aspects of reality.

Nothing else mattered but my baby and my milk. I really got obsessed and my marriage began to suffer. I know now that I did experience some postpartum depression(PPD). My husband felt (and had been) neglected and I was an emotional mess. I never had thoughts of harming my baby, so it never occurred to me that I had any PPD. However, my mother noticed it and finally decided to come to my rescue. She lived at the opposite part of our state, but she dropped everything and she came to my rescue.

She told me that she would stay until God healed my heart and the depression lifted. Tears come pouring down my face even now as I relive those painful days. I can remember how relieved I felt that someone cared enough to take my pain seriously. I felt validated. I felt that I mattered. I felt loved.

During her stay, my mom held me, she cooked and cleaned for me, she cried with me and wiped away my tears. And during the day she would pray. She prayed out loud, quoted Scripture, and she sang worship songs. It didn't take long for the atmosphere in my house to change.

There is just something special in the compassion that a mother has for her child that is so like the heart of God. I believe God heard her desperate pleas and He honored her prayers. Two weeks later, she packed her bags and left behind a joyful daughter. My mother's prayers broke the depression over my life. Never underestimate the prayers of a Momma when she prays for her children. Something special happens!

So, my precious little boy will be four years old this June. He is such a precious gift from the Lord! We do want more children and we have been waiting for a couple of years now. So I will wait and I will trust and I will cling to my Jesus! His timing is perfect and although I don't like or understand the delay, I trust that He has my best interest in mind, because I know He loves me. He loves me more than my momma, and that's hard to wrap my mind around!

Rejoice with those who rejoice,
and weep with those who weep.
Romans 12:15 NASB

Adoption

I wanted to include a section on adoption in this book for women who feel that God is leading them to adopt a child. Sometimes, a husband and wife may feel that even though they can get pregnant, the best choice for them is adoption or sometimes, when they can't get pregnant, instead of trying fertility routes, they believe that adoption is the road that God would have them take.

Adoption is a very special event. You are choosing a child to come and live with you. The parallels can be seen with what God did for us by sending Jesus to the cross. He gave up His own Son so that He could have all of us. It's amazing when you think of it that way. Would you give up your own child to add many more to your family? Most of us would have to answer, "No".

Merriam-Webster defines adopt as "to take by choice into a relationship." It must be a very special feeling to know that you were chosen into a family. Ephesians 1:5 NIV says, "He predestined us to be adopted as his sons through Jesus Christ, in accordance with his pleasure and will."

If you feel that the Lord is leading you to adopt a child, then know that He will bless the transition for your family. I have seen many people who thought they had tried everything to have their own child, adopt and then end up pregnant years later. What an added blessing! God is always faithful and He will take care of His own.

Blessed Beyond Measure

by Margie

In the beginning of our marriage, we struggled to get pregnant. After a surgery and three years later, we had our first daughter. Fourteen months later, we had our second daughter. Again, we struggled to conceive our third child. This time, I had another surgery and fertility treatments. Four and a half years later, we had our son. Due to medical reasons, we were told this would be our last child. We were devastated. My husband and I had always thought we'd like to have four to six kids.

We decided that we would like to someday adopt, but we didn't know where to start. At that time, adoption was almost unheard of in our background. Nine years had passed when friends of ours told us they were going to become foster parents with the hopes to adopt. Instantly, we decided to foster as well. By now, we were in our late 30's and thought we were too old to adopt, so we thought we'd foster.

We got certified and received our first placement, premature twin girls, straight from the hospital. We fostered them for 15 months and they changed our lives in a way we hadn't expected. As soon as we got the girls, we knew they would come up for adoption. We started praying for them and God moved mightily. When we got them, they couldn't hear; they failed three hearing tests. We just kept praying.

At four months, when the twins passed their hearing tests with flying colors. By this time, we had fallen in love with them and had decided that we wanted to adopt them, so we started praying that God would reveal it to us if He wanted us to adopt them.

174

One day, when the twins were seven months old, as I was praying over them, I felt like the Lord spoke to me and said the girls were not going to stay. I couldn't believe what I had just heard. I didn't say anything to anyone. I just kept praying and questioning God, *Why?* On the third night, as I was done praying, the Lord asked, "I thought you wanted the very best for them?" At that point, I told my husband, and within a week, we had met a Christian couple who was wanting to adopt the girls. At first, it was very hard to accept. But we did want what was best for us all. It took another eight months for them to be placed in their adoptive home.

We tried to prepare for them leaving, but there's no way to prepare for something like that. When they left, we were just not prepared for the big hole they left in our lives. When people would see us, they would say that the girls were so blessed to have us in their lives, but the truth was we were blessed to have them in our life. We learned so much from them. Our family suffered great loss. They had been so much a part of our life and we missed them so much. They taught us what true love really was. This is the hardest thing our family has had to go through. We then decided to take a break from fostering.

After a hard year of missing the twins, we told CPS that if they could get us another set of newborn twins they thought would come up for adoption, we'd like to try again. Our home developer, Jan, was just the sweetest lady with a very kind heart who truly wanted the best for the children. Jan told us that we would be the first family she called if they got twins. On January 20th, we got the call we were waiting for. It was Jan, and they had a set of newborn boy-girl twins! We felt confident that they would come up for adoption since the mother had given up previous children.

On January 22nd, we picked up Isaiah from the hospital, 26 days old and 4 lbs 5oz. Three days later we got to pick up Chloe. She was 29 days old and also 4 lbs 5 oz. They were beautiful! We were so excited, but also terrified of falling in love with them and then losing them to the parents or other family members. I seriously started praying that these babies would be ours and that God would make it happen.

One day, while I was visiting with another friend of ours who was fostering to adopt as well, she told me how she prayed for their foster children's parents. She prayed that they would clean up their life because she knew that would be the very best thing for the children. My heart was immediately convicted. I realized how selfish I was being, just wanting my will to be done, not God's. At that time, I changed my prayer. I, too, started praying for the twins' mom, praying she would change her life.

Their mother had two supervised visits a week with the twins. At five months, she started missing visits. When we got the notice for our next court date, we started praying that God would convict her and take her peace from her to make the right decision for the twins.

On our way to court, my husband Neil said, " Wouldn't it be neat if she just voluntarily relinquished her rights?"

"It's a nice thought but it's not going to happen," I said. When we walked into the court room, the mom was crying hysterically. She and the case worker started walking out of the court room.

As they passed me, our case worker motioned for me to follow. As soon as we got out of the room, the mom grabbed me by both arms and said, " I have had no peace. I can't sleep.

All I can think about is doing what's best for the twins. If I give up my rights, will you adopt them?" I couldn't believe what I was hearing; it was exactly as we had prayed! I started crying and told her we would. Those words weren't as sweet as I thought they would be.

In order for us to become parents again, another family would have to suffer loss. The verse, "'One sows and another reaps' is true. I sent you to reap what you have not worked for others have done the hard work and you have reaped the benefits of their labors" (John 4:37,38 NIV), immediately popped into my head. She went on saying that she had nothing to offer them and she knew we loved them and were able to give them the life she wanted them to have. My heart broke for her.

We were so excited that the twins would be ours, but the birth mom disappeared after that, and never actually signed the papers. So the court had to terminate her rights. She was always in our hearts and prayers.

One day, I had the feeling that she was pregnant again, so I called the case worker about it and she said she had asked the mom earlier and she said no. On the morning of February 12th, she was heavy on my heart. I started praying for her but I couldn't get peace. I called my husband at work and told him about it. He told me to call the case worker and see if they had heard from her since she disappeared seven months ago.

I called the case worker and she said, "No we haven't. Why, what's up?" I told her that I couldn't stop thinking about her and couldn't shake the feeling that something was going on. She said if they heard from her, she'd call me right away.

About an hour later, she called me back and said that the hospital just informed her that the mom gave birth to another baby boy at 12:06 P.M. They asked if we would be interested in taking him, too. With the twins being only 13 months old, not walking, and still on bottles, we weren't sure we could handle another baby. But God had other plans. We didn't have peace until we decided to take him.

On Valentine's Day, they brought us our beautiful new baby, only two days old. We knew then that our family was complete. We now have three boys and three girls. Our whole family feels so blessed to have them in our lives. Looking back, it's hard to believe that God answered all our prayers and gave us the desires of our hearts. We are very grateful to God for that and for the awesome power of prayer!

For God is the one who provides seed for
the farmer and then bread to eat. In the same way,
he will provide and increase your resources and
then produce a great harvest of generosity in you.
2 Corinthians 9:10

A Final Word

As this book comes to a close, I hope that you have gained an understanding of God's heart for you. He loves you so much and is ready to grant you what you ask. I pray that the stories you have read and the scriptures I have shared will be an encouragement to you. If you have never received Jesus into your life as your Savior and Lord and desire to, please read the salvation prayer on the next page and let me know that you did.

You can contact me through our website:
www.harrisonhouse.com

All information on How Your Baby is Growing and How Your Life is Changing can be found at:

www.babycenter.com
www.babyzone.com

God's blessings to you and your growing family!

Prayer of Salvation

God loves you—no matter who you are, no matter what your past. God loves you so much that He gave His one and only begotten Son for you. The Bible tells us that "...whoever believes in him shall not perish but have eternal life" (John 3:16 NIV). Jesus laid down His life and rose again so that we could spend eternity with Him in heaven and experience His absolute best on earth. If you would like to receive Jesus into your life, say the following prayer out loud and mean it from your heart.

Heavenly Father, I come to You admitting that I am a sinner. Right now, I choose to turn away from sin, and I ask You to cleanse me of all unrighteousness. I believe that Your Son, Jesus, died on the cross to take away my sins. I also believe that He rose again from the dead so that I might be forgiven of my sins and made righteous through faith in Him. I call upon the name of Jesus Christ to be the Savior and Lord of my life. Jesus, I choose to follow You and ask that You fill me with the power of the Holy Spirit. I declare that right now I am a child of God. I am free from sin and full of the righteousness of God. I am saved in Jesus' name. Amen.

If you prayed this prayer to receive Jesus Christ as your Savior for the first time, please contact us on the Web at:

www.harrisonhouse.com to receive a free book.

Or you may write to us at

Harrison House • P.O. Box 35035 • Tulsa, Oklahoma 74153

Fast. Easy. Convenient.

For the latest Harrison House product information and author news, look no further than your computer. All the details on our powerful, life-changing products are just a click away. New releases, E-mail subscriptions, testimonies, monthly specials—find it all in one place. Visit harrisonhouse.com today!

harrisonhouse

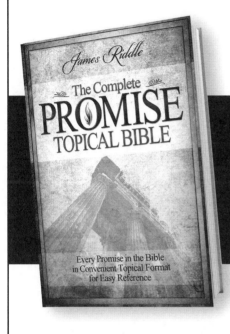

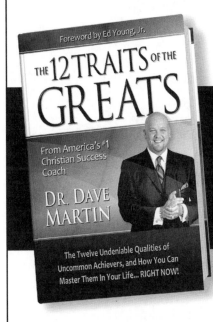